BREAKFAST
AT
MONSANTO'S

*Is Roundup in our food
making us fatter, sicker, and
sadder?*

Lee A. Evslin, M.D.

Ohana Publishing

BREAKFAST AT MONSANTO'S
Is Roundup in our food making us fatter, sicker, and sadder?

Lee A Evslin, M.D.

ISBN: 9781735273112

Makai Ola LLC
4-1184 Kuhio Hwy
Kapaa, HI 96746

Ohana Publishing

Quotes from *Silent Spring* by Rachel Carson
Copyright © 1962 by Rachel Carson
Copyright © Renewal by Roger Christie
Reprinted by permission of Frances Collin, Trustee

Graphs from Swanson N, Leu A, et al. Genetically engineered crops,
glyphosate and the deterioration of health in the United States of America.
J Org Systems. 2014. Reprinted by permission of Andre Leu

Trademark Acknowledgements
Roundup* Roundup Ready* Registered Trademarks of Monsanto Company.
Bayer Purchased Monsanto 2018

Cover Design by Makai Ola LLC

DEDICATION

To my wife and soulmate, Micki. She sets an example for us all, living life with a fierce intensity and integrity (and she made me write this book).

AUTHOR'S NOTE

This book is a discussion of the scientific evidence regarding the health risks of pesticides, including the various herbicides that contain glyphosate as an active ingredient. This is an issue that potentially affects everyone because of the prevalence of glyphosate in our environment, in our food, and in our bodies.

The most familiar example of an herbicide that contains glyphosate is a line of products manufactured by the company formerly called Monsanto, which was acquired by Bayer AG in 2018, and sold under the Roundup family of trademarks.

Roundup products have been the subject of high-profile litigation and ongoing media coverage for many years now. This book is my contribution to the public conversation about Roundup in particular and the larger public health issues that may arise from the widespread use of pesticides and genetically-engineered crops designed to resist pesticides.

All third-party trademarks, including the Roundup family of marks, are used in this book for purposes of identification only. This book is independently authored and published, and no affiliation with the third-party trademark owners is claimed or implied.

TABLE OF CONTENTS

IMPORTANT TERMS

Bayer AG: The corporation which purchased Monsanto in 2018. The lawsuits mentioned in this book are being settled by Bayer AG but often reference Monsanto and therefore both companies are named in discussions of these cases.

Chemical-seed companies: In the 20th century some of the largest chemical companies in the world began to buy seed companies. These acquisitions allowed a merging of their pesticide products with the development of seed strains. Monsanto became a leader in this field with the development of its Roundup-resistant genetically engineered crops.

Glyphosate: The active ingredient in Roundup and in other similar chemical formulations.

Glyphosate-Based Herbicides (GBHs): These are chemical formulations similar to Roundup in that they contain glyphosate as their active ingredient.

Monsanto: The chemical seed company that patented and produced Roundup. They also produced the genetically engineered (GMO) crops that are able to resist Roundup. Monsanto was purchased by Bayer AG in 2018.

Pesticide: A pesticide is any substance used to kill, repel, or control certain forms of plant or animal life that are considered to be pests. Pesticides include herbicides for destroying weeds and other unwanted vegetation, insecticides for controlling a wide variety of insects, fungicides used to prevent the growth of molds and mildew, disinfectants for preventing the spread of bacteria, and compounds used to control mice and rats. Because of the widespread use of agricultural chemicals in food production, people are exposed to low levels of pesticide residues through their diets. Scientists do not yet have a clear understanding of the health effects of these pesticide residues. (National Institutes of Health)

Roundup: The trademark of a chemical formulation patented by Monsanto and having glyphosate as its active ingredient. It also contains other chemicals designed to make this formulation more effective at killing vegetation.

INTRODUCTION: WHY ARE WE SO SICK?

The central problem of our age has therefore become the con-
tamination of man's total environment with such substances
of incredible potential for harm—substances that accumulate
in the tissues of plants and animals and even penetrate the
germ cells to shatter or alter the very material of heredity
upon which the shape of the future depends.

—Rachel Carson, *Silent Spring* (1962)

We called the clinic *Makai Ola*, which is Hawaiian for "healing by the sea." My office was in a vintage plantation-style home on the ocean's edge, surrounded by the ocean's sound and the waves' reflected light. Most of my professional life had been on Kaua'i, but this small private practice was the realization of a dream I had held for years.

As a pediatrician with training in adult medicine and a lifelong interest in wellness, I've been fascinated by the question of what makes one person well and another chronically ill. People of all ages came to our clinic with interests in exploring healthier lifestyles. I saw patients, lectured on nutrition, and worked with groups who were pursuing new ways to eat and feel better.

Most of my professional career prior to this had been spent in more traditional settings. Over the course of thirty-five years, I had worked in the island's midsize medical group as a primary care physician with an interest in nutrition, as the CEO of the medical group, and then as CEO of the adjoining hospital. After years of a professional life immersed in the administrative challenges of keeping a rural hospital and medical group up to date in terms of equipment and standards, and an intense few years leading the implementation of electronic medical records into a statewide healthcare system, it was a great pleasure for me to return to practicing medicine, particularly in such an idyllic setting.

But after my return to full-time practice, one question kept reverberating through my mind: Why are people sicker now than they used to be? How did everyone get so fat? And that wasn't all. Kids were having many more behavioral problems. Autism had skyrocketed. Greater than 50 percent of adults in America had at least one chronic medical condition, and the incidence of many chronic diseases was worsening. And perhaps even more alarming, for the first time in modern history, the life expectancy of the average American was going down.

Like most of us, I've listened as different theories explaining these disturbing medical developments were proposed. The suggested causes often include ideas such as sugar poisoning, the opioid epidemic, gluten and grain poisoning, poisoning by processed foods in general, cell phone and screen addictions, and electromagnetic frequency exposure.

In 2012, I found a clue to another possible reason for our collective ill health. It was in a policy statement issued by the American Academy of Pediatrics (AAP). These policy statements are created and distributed to help guide those of us who care for children. They cover most topics of importance in the healthcare of children and are so well respected that they set the standards for pediatric care around the world. That November, the AAP issued a technical report, followed by a policy statement on the topic of pesticide exposure in children.[1,2] The statement began this way:

> Pesticides represent a large group of products designed to kill or harm living organisms ... making them inherently toxic. Beyond acute poisoning, the influences of *low-level* exposures on child health are of increasing concern.
> (Italics added)

The reports detailed the potential dangers of childhood exposure to pesticides and the actions pediatricians might take in response. These two position papers presented a concept that was new to most pediatricians. In our medical training, we learn about the dangers of poisoning by pesticides if a child inadvertently drinks some of it or is mistakenly sprayed. But most of us have not been trained to consider the danger of chronic low-level exposures. It was shocking to learn of the long list of medical conditions associated with the low-level exposure one might get from food, from pesticide use in the home or garden, or just by living near agricultural fields.

These reports from the AAP were published at the same time that the island of Kaua'i was going through an incredibly divisive period. On the Westside of Kaua'i, four chemical-seed companies had test fields for GMO crops. These companies, plus a coffee plantation, were allegedly spraying eighteen tons of restricted use pesticides (RUPs) annually in a relatively small area within a fragile Hawaiian ecosystem.

This island battle centered on a county legislative bill entitled 2491. This bill called for (1) no-spray buffer zones around schools and other places people congregate, (2) the right to know what was being sprayed where, and (3) notification of spraying activities for those that lived near the fields. One might think that these types of recommendations are pretty reasonable. But even as these were similar to solutions discussed in the AAP publications, the vitriol expressed by people on both sides of the issue was explosive, at times even frightening. Adding to the discord was that many local people depended on these companies for work, and the people most vocal in their opposition to these companies were often more recent island implants. Many of the activists lived on another part of the island. The debate became so divisive that politicians and others reported receiving threats of violence.

Two acrimonious years went by. The saga of that bill seeking no-spray buffer zones has been well described in several film documentaries with dramatic titles such as *Poisoning Paradise*. The bill was passed but was later overturned by the courts; it was determined that the County of Kauai's ordinances in this situation were preempted by state laws. Despite the ultimate failure of the bill and because of the continued spraying around the state, pesticide exposure became and still is a statewide concern.

■ ■ ■

In 2014, I was asked by the lead investigator to join eight others with varying pertinent advanced degrees and participate in a state-commissioned, fact-finding task force. This group was created to evaluate the possibility that the people and/or the environment on the Westside of Kaua'i were being harmed by pesticides. It was estimated that the project would take a year.

I began what amounted to a mini-residency in pesticides and health. I combed the medical literature while meeting and speaking to some of the country's foremost researchers on the subject. It was an intense fourteen months. By design, task force members included representatives from different sides of the Kaua'i conflict. Two participants worked for the seed companies; one participant was retired from the University of Hawai'i, and as a UH researcher, he had worked with the seed companies. Another was an organic farmer; another was a retired Harvard physician who had played a prominent role in environmental issues; and the rest of us represented other viewpoints. Leading this seriously biased group (biased in all directions) was Peter Adler, a trained mediator and an expert in running joint fact-finding task forces representing opposing views.

Our task force interactions were full of drama. The UH researcher dropped out of the task force months before we completed our investigation. The two seed company employees precipitously resigned ten days before the final publication. They quit within minutes of each other. The three left the task force, stating that they disagreed with the process but leaving a strong impression that they—and perhaps the companies they worked for—had significant problems accepting the validity of the scientific data we were collecting. Somehow, though, we ended up producing a well-balanced review of pesticide usage on the Westside, including its potential impact on both health and the environment. We offered recommendations for safer usage.[3] Following the instructions of the lead investigator, the task force finished the report as if the missing members with their chemical company leanings were still in the room.

My immersion into the science of pesticides and health led me to join a growing group of researchers and practitioners who believe that the heavy use of pesticides is harming our planet and its inhabitants. Current scientific literature on the subject is sounding the alarm. Rapidly increasing evidence suggests that even when *used properly* pesticides are toxic to humans and the environment. What has also become obvious is that—similar to the cigarette campaigns of years past—statements issued by the chemical-seed companies are often in shocking conflict with current scientific research.

The road to scientific consensus is long and twisted, and too often big money has the power to distort or delay important findings. Concerns over our toxic environment have led to strongly worded statements by not only the American Academy of Pediatrics but also the American College of Obstetrics-Gynecology.[4] The International Federation of Obstetrics-Gynecology in collaboration with the national Ob-Gyn organizations from the United States, United Kingdom, and Canada have gone so far as to say that women who are pregnant, breastfeeding, or desire to become pregnant should eat *"pesticide-free"* produce.[5] This book describes why pesticide-free produce should possibly be a priority for all of us.

I will also explore in depth one particular pesticide which is popularly known as Roundup. Its active ingredient is glyphosate and it is now found in many similar commercial preparations known as glyphosate-based herbicides (GBHs).

Roundup has been covered extensively in the news over the past several years due to the allegation that it causes cancer. Numerous court cases involving people who sprayed it have received a great deal of attention. The research in this book highlights the less-well-known fact that since the mid-1990s, GBHs have become pervasive in our food supply. An important question that has not yet been satisfactorily answered is, what are GBHs doing to our health as we eat and drink them and are exposed to them in nearby spraying activities?

Summary

1. Some of the most important questions of our times are the following: Why are the health statistics worsening in many developed nations of the world? Why is the life expectancy going down for the first time in the modern era in America? Why has the incidence of obesity skyrocketed in so many developed nations and particularly in America?

2. There is developing concern and emerging research defining the role that environmental toxins, including pesticides, may have in our worsening health statistics.

3. Glyphosate, the active ingredient of the herbicide Roundup, is by far the most heavily sprayed pesticide in the history of the world. Exposure from spraying it is increasingly recognized as a danger; less well known, but increasingly well researched, is that exposure to glyphosate in our food and neighborhoods may also be a health risk.

1

GLYPHOSATE AND CHRONIC DISEASES, A STRIKING CORRELATION

*I contend, furthermore, that we have allowed these
chemicals to be used with little or no advance investigation
of their effect on soil, water, wildlife, and man himself.
Future generations are unlikely to condone our lack of
prudent concern for the integrity of the natural world that
supports all life.*

—Rachel Carson, *Silent Spring (1962)*

As pediatricians, we learn early in our careers to carefully look at a child and their caretaker with all our senses wide open. Small children cannot tell you what bothers them, and our ultimate diagnosis often significantly depends on our first impression of how sick or not sick they appear and how worried or not worried their caretaker appears. In the days before vaccines for meningitis, we frequently diagnosed and treated this condition. Sometimes the symptoms were quite subtle. Missing the clues and delaying treatment could result in a child dying or becoming brain damaged. Good pediatricians are powerfully attuned to first impressions and a kind of gestalt about the child in front of them.

My daily routine is walking on a bike path by the ocean. I walk near condo units that are filled with tourists. They come out in the morning with their coffee mugs, newly purchased shorts, and aloha shirts to enjoy the sunrise and the early morning trade winds. My overwhelming first impression is how unhealthy so many of them appear. Unfortunately, the signs are not particularly subtle. Our island guests are often heavy with protuberant stomachs, moving slowly with swollen ankles, and not uncommonly using walkers or canes.

Americans are no longer healthy. Staggering statistics show that we are spending $3.7 trillion a year on healthcare—twice the amount on a per capita basis as any country in Europe. Two-thirds of us are overweight, and 50 percent of American adults have at least one chronic medical condition.

In 2014, the *Journal of Organic Systems* published a fascinating and—if valid—alarming study.[6] At the heart of the paper are a series of graphs showing the increase in glyphosate use in the United States. Superimposed on the charts are increases in cancer, as well as other chronic diseases affecting Americans. The correlations and the statistical significance of the associations are striking. The study's lead author was Dr. Nancy Swanson. She has a PhD in physics, worked as a staff scientist for the United States Navy, holds five U.S. patents, and is the author of over thirty scientific publications.

It is very well known that "correlation does not prove causation." Certainly, this has been endlessly repeated by the companies producing these chemicals. Just because two events occur together in time does not prove that one causes the other. An example frequently given is that night invariably follows day, but that is not proof that day causes night.

But seeing a correlation in the world of medicine and science—particularly one with a high statistical correlation and the knowledge that all pesticides have toxic potential—is concerning. At the very least, it should prompt studies to determine whether or not there is a cause-and-effect relationship. For instance, years ago people began to notice that smokers suffered from a greater incidence of lung cancer and chronic lung diseases, but whether smoking actually caused lung disease was furiously debated for years. Finally, it was proven without a doubt that cigarette smoking causes lung cancer and lung disease. Eventually, the accumulation of animal and human studies made the conclusion undeniable.

■ ■ ■

Glyphosate is the active ingredient of the herbicide called Roundup. It kills plants by disrupting a major metabolic pathway not found in mammals, and for that reason it is purported to be safe for mammals, including humans. Glyphosate was introduced in 1974 and was first used on fields, but not applied directly to food crops. In the 1980s, the American agrochemical and agricultural biotechnology corporation Monsanto realized that farmers could also use glyphosate to dry certain food crops right before harvest. Killing these crops made them easier to harvest as they would dry out and be less bulky. It was used (and still is) with increasing frequency on a large number of foods including wheat, oats, rice, seeds, beans, peas, sugarcane, and potatoes.

In the 1990s, a second explosion of use occurred as Monsanto came up with another lucrative idea. They isolated a genetic trait from a type of bacteria found in soil. This particular trait in the bacteria protected it from dying when exposed to Roundup. Company scientists took this trait and inserted it into the genes of corn, soy, canola, cotton, and more recently sugar beets. When sprayed with Roundup, this trait from a non-plant protected these plants from dying.

These are the so-called Roundup-resistant GMO crops. The miracle about these crops is that a farmer can spray Roundup right on these plants and the crop will not die, but all the weeds around the crop will die off. For farmers, this resulted in a much less labor-intensive way to grow food. They no longer needed to till the fields, pull weeds by hand, or carefully spray around the crops to free their fields from weeds. These days, most of the nonorganic soy, corn, canola and sugar beets produced in America are of the GMO type.

These new uses for glyphosate (killing and drying certain plants right before harvest and spraying but not killing other food crops, just their weeds) meant that from the early 1990s, our food has become vastly different from any other time in human history. We had sugar, food additives, and fat-filled junk foods for years before glyphosate; we even have had other pesticides on our crops. But in the early 1990s, for the first time, our nonorganic foods were being served up with particularly generous helpings of one particular herbicide.

This first graph from the startling paper in the *Journal of Organic Systems* shows actual tons of glyphosate sprayed on corn, soy, and cotton crops in America. Glyphosate is not only on our food; it is also on the material making our clothes, tampons, and other items. The annual amount sprayed on these crops went from almost zero tons in 1990 to ninety thousand tons in 2010.

Glyphosate Applied to Corn, Cotton, and Soy Crops in the Surveyed States

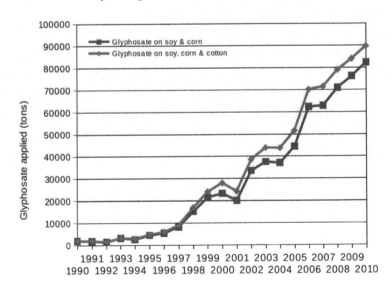

The next set of graphs are also from the same study. They demonstrate the increase in the amounts of glyphosate sprayed on corn and soy and the increase in GMO crops in general over time. They compare that increase with the increase in certain medical conditions. The amounts sprayed on just these two crops is merely a fraction of what is sprayed across America. As mentioned, glyphosate is also sprayed on non-GMO crops such as oats and wheat to dry them before harvest.

The solid yellow bars represent statistics for the medical condition being examined, and the red and blue lines depict the increase in the percentage of GMO crops and increase in the amount of glyphosate sprayed over the years being examined. The green line is the trend before the increase in glyphosate.

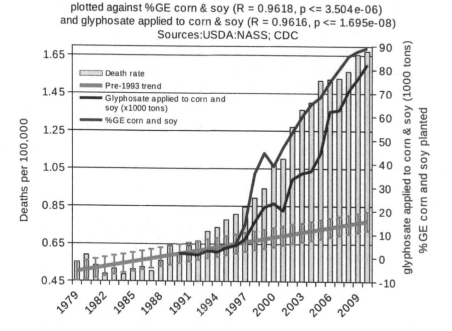

Age Adjusted Deaths due to Obesity (ICD E66 & 278)

plotted against %GE corn & soy (R = 0.9618, p <= 3.504e-06)
and glyphosate applied to corn & soy (R = 0.9616, p <= 1.695e-08)
Sources:USDA:NASS; CDC

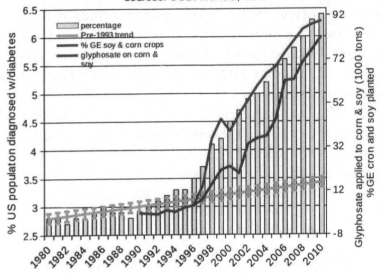

Prevalence of Diabetes in US (age adjusted)
plotted against glyphosate applied to corn & soy (R = 0.971, p <= 9.24e-09)
along with %GE corn & soy grown in US (R=0.9826, p <= 5.169e-07)
sources: USDA:NASS; CDC

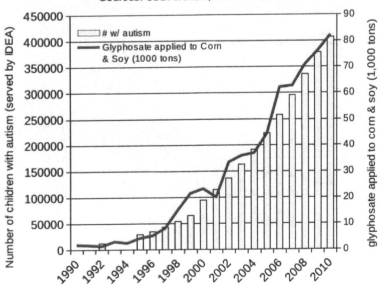

Number of children (6-21yrs) with autism served by IDEA
plotted against glyphosate use on corn & soy (R = 0.9893, p <= 3.629e-07)
Sources: USDA:NASS; USDE:IDEA

This tight and worrisome correlation between the increased incidence of a disease and the increased use of glyphosate on our food was graphed by these same authors in a similar fashion for the following conditions:

- Cancer of the thyroid, kidney, bladder, renal pelvis, liver, bile duct
- Alzheimer's, Parkinson's, senile dementia
- Inflammatory bowel disease, death from intestinal infections
- Deaths from hypertension, strokes, obesity, abnormalities of lipid metabolism, end-stage renal disease

(The graphs for these conditions can be found in Appendix A)

The large amount of sugar in American diets is without a doubt one of the causes of obesity and ill health in America. (In Appendix A, there is also a graph of sweetener use in the U.S.) It is important to note that sweetener (cane, beet, and corn) delivery has actually come down since the late 1990s, while the prevalence of the diseases plotted in the graphs continues to go up.

The significant correlations graphed above should concern us all. The questions for the scientific community are many. Does the scientific evidence in existing studies demonstrate a causal relationship between the increase in glyphosate use and the increase in our population's ill health? What additional research is needed to prove or disprove this concept?

As consumers, we must ask ourselves whether this correlation of ill health with the use of glyphosate is enough to make us buy mostly organic foods.

If glyphosate is proven to be one of the drivers of ill-health, its role does not decrease the dangers of smoking, eating ultra-processed foods, lack of exercise, and all of the other known causes of chronic diseases but it will give us one more explanation for why we have become such a sickly nation.

Summary

1. Starting in the 1980s, Roundup was sprayed on grain crops such as wheat and oats prior to harvest to act as a drying agent.

2. In the mid-1990s, GMO Roundup-ready crops were created and popularized. These particular GMO crops can be sprayed with Roundup and the crops will not be injured. Only the weeds will die.

3. The result of these two uses of Roundup means that since the mid-1990s, there was a dramatic increase in herbicides on our food. Nonorganic soy, corn, sugar beets and canola are the main Roundup-ready GMO crops. Wheat, oats, rice, seeds, beans, peas, sugar cane, potatoes and many other non-GMO crops may be sprayed before harvest for the drying effect.

4. In 2014, a paper was published showing a correlation in time between the increased spraying of glyphosate-based herbicides (GBHs) such as Roundup and a wide range of diseases including cancers, obesity, inflammatory conditions, and even autism.

5. The conclusion of this chapter is that the correlation in time is concerning but not proof that GBHs such as Roundup causes any of these conditions. Scientists need to examine the existing studies and design future studies to prove or disprove that GBHs are playing a role in the worsening health statistics.

2

THE SAFETY OF GLYPHOSATE
IN YOUR CHILD'S CHEERIOS

The legend that the herbicides are toxic only to plants and so
pose no threat to animal life has been widely disseminated,
but unfortunately it is not true.

—Rachel Carson, Silent Spring (1962)

In 2015, the International Agency for Research on Cancer (IARC), a committee of the United Nations, stated that glyphosate "probably" causes cancer. This designation is still fiercely debated, but throughout 2018 and 2019, landmark court cases were decided against Bayer AG—the new owner of Monsanto. The first case involved Dwayne Johnson, a man who had sprayed Roundup for years as part of his job. Dying of lymphoma, he was awarded $287 million by a jury. Another plaintiff was actually awarded $2 billion. These dramatic jury verdicts are a reflection of both the weight of evidence presented on the cancer-causing properties of this herbicide and of an alleged coverup of this toxicity by Monsanto. In June 2020, Bayer agreed to a settlement of $10 billion to resolve more than 100,000 lawsuits alleging that its weedkiller, Roundup, causes cancer.

While these are sad and often tragic cases, they only involve people who reported heavy exposure to GBHs through spraying activities and then developed cancer. However, looking at the graphs on the preceding pages leads one to the possibility that these cancer cases are just the tip of an enormous iceberg of ill health.

Although many people spray GBHs, the majority of people in the developed world consume GBHs in their food or are exposed by the spraying of others. If indeed these chemicals play a role in the dramatic increase in health problems across the world, the companies producing Roundup-like herbicides are poisoning the world.

Perhaps that sounds too strong, immediately categorizing me as a wild-eyed environmentalist. But the definition of a poison is, "A substance which is capable of causing illness or death when ingested or absorbed." Day by day, the evidence gets stronger that glyphosate formulations could be making us ill.

The disparity between the scientific literature and the statements of the chemical-seed companies about pesticides became strikingly clear during the fourteen months our task force examined potential harms from pesticides on Kaua'i. Our mandate was to look at the pesticides called restricted use pesticides (RUPs). These substances are known to be particularly toxic, and their use is tightly controlled.

Produced by Dow Chemical, chlorpyrifos is one of these regulated pesticides. It is of particular concern to me as a pediatrician because it is a known neurotoxin and very dangerous to the developing fetus. There are hundreds of studies concerning its toxicity—several are particularly well-regarded and well-publicized. The CHAMCO study in California and a Columbia University study in New York are perhaps the most well known. These studies tracked children whose mothers were exposed to chlorpyrifos during pregnancy.[7,8] The exposures were from household spraying and spraying in nearby agricultural fields. Carefully monitored for years, the children were shown to have permanent changes to their brains and delays in mental development. The degree of these adverse effects was in direct proportion to the amounts of the pesticide found in the mother's urine and the baby's cord blood.

As our task force reviewed chlorpyrifos, I felt as though I'd entered an alternate reality. The medical and scientific literature could not have been more explicit about the dangers of this chemical, yet the biotechnology companies and their scientists acted as if these studies did not exist. Syngenta even claimed that chlorpyrifos was safe enough to be regularly sprayed from a large pesticide boom truck just 60 feet from the open windows of a Kaua'i middle school. It took the Hawaii State Teachers Association and a lawsuit to bring this distressing practice to an end.[9]

This brings us back to glyphosate. It is considered so safe that it is not even a restricted use pesticide. Monsanto's statements in the past have included the following:

> Glyphosate has a more than 40-year history of safe use. Over those four decades, researchers have conducted more than 800 scientific studies and reviews that support the safe use of glyphosate.

In 2018 and 2019, the courts repeatedly ruled against glyphosate's safety. But Monsanto's current parent company, Bayer AG, continues to claim that the courts and a growing public concern about glyphosate and Roundup are based on neither fact nor science.

Are they in a twilight zone of truth, or could they be correct, that glyphosate is as safe as they say?

■ ■ ■

I have followed the glyphosate controversies since 2014. After I learned that glyphosate is patented as an antibiotic and a chelating agent as well as an herbicide, I became interested in what it is doing to our gut and skin. What adverse effects might low doses of this antibiotic have on the ten billion bacteria that live in and on our body?

Nancy Swanson's graphs and her study encouraged me to widen my search concerning glyphosate's toxicity. Examining the medical literature on any topic has become easier in this age of the internet. For example, Pubmed is a free computerized portal to the National Library of Medicine (NLM). As of December 2018, PubMed had more than 29.1 million records going back to 1966, and a less complete list going back to 1806. In addition, they add about 500,000 new citations each year. Pubmed uses stringent criteria for the journals they index. The journals must meet high standards of scientific credibility.

In 2019, if you went to Pubmed and typed in "glyphosate toxicity," you quickly discovered that there were more than 960 articles on the subject. More than one half had been published in the previous five years.

Of the studies published between 2017 and 2019, the vast majority revealed glyphosate's toxic effects on a wide range of organisms—from bacteria in soil, to amphibians, to various cell lines, and to humans. In March 2019, I completed a review of the most recent 240 articles. I calculated how many papers described glyphosate's toxicity versus how many demonstrated proof of no or minimal toxicity. Of these 240 articles, about 10 percent showed no harm from glyphosate.

Reviewing this large number of articles made me question where were the 800 studies that are described by Monsanto as showing glyphosate's safety. These most recent studies were not reassuring.

Research outside of Pubmed revealed more about the missing 800 studies that demonstrated *safety*. A large number of these studies were done many years ago.[10] They were performed by the chemical company or by firms hired by the company to do this testing. Furthermore, their results were often not published in peer-reviewed periodicals or indexed in Pubmed. The companies maintain the results of these tests are proprietary, and that this material is privileged information. In other words, much of these companies' evidence showing their product is safe is top secret information that cannot be shared.

As I further analyzed the studies purported to show safety, the following information added to my concern:

1. Although the earlier studies are mostly held as private information, researchers have been able to analyze some of the data. A team of researchers from the United Kingdom and Brazil looked at some of the private data revealed in a government publication.[11] They found that in a rat study, the data clearly showed a statistically significant increase in tumors. Monsanto's published results from the same data did not reveal this increase.

2. As mentioned, a large number of the tests used to demonstrate safety were done decades ago, and a significant number of the current studies showing harm use much more modern testing methodologies than were available at that time.

3. Most importantly, researchers have also shown that GBHs are contaminating *all* the diets fed to rats in many of these studies.[12] Studies comparing health effects from GMO or non-GMO diets in rats frequently have the same amount of glyphosate in *both* diets. So, instead of demonstrating that a GMO diet with high levels of glyphosate is unhealthy or healthy for rats, the studies show that labeling a food non-GMO is not a good way to know if your food contains GBHs.

It is important to understand that many drugs and chemicals approved for use by the government have their preliminary studies done or paid for by the companies producing these products. This makes sense, as universities or researchers with less bias are not going to spend the money researching a drug or chemical that may never reach the approval stage.

But at least in the world of medicine, once a drug is approved, it is fair game for further research. There is a long list of drugs that have been found harmful in follow-up studies. They were subsequently taken off the market or became limited in their approved use. Estrogen is a perfect example. It was widely used for women going through menopause. The evidence became increasingly strong that it also increased the risk of cancer. Estrogen is now used much more sparingly in the United States. Even so, while its producers accepted the restrictions in the United States and accepted that there is a cancer risk, they continued to market it aggressively in countries that had less stringent guidelines. In the field of pesticides, the EPA reviews a pesticide every fifteen years. However, when studies come out in the interim that show toxicity, there is often a well-organized, well-funded corporate effort to discredit these newer studies. Under pressure, the EPA will re-review a drug sooner than fifteen years. Often though, it takes a court case to force the EPA to reconsider a chemical.

Summary

1. There is an international debate raging about whether glyphosate-based herbicides (GBHs) such as Roundup cause cancer. There are tens of thousands of lawsuits pending with the claim that spraying GBHs caused cancer. There have been multimillion-dollar judgments against Monsanto-Bayer. These judgments have been in favor of people who sprayed or were exposed to GBHs. Bayer has made a multibillion-dollar offer to settle these cases.

2. Thousands of people may have sprayed GBHs, yet millions are consuming these substances in their food. Many health conditions have worsened since the 1990s when glyphosate became a regular part of the world's food supply.

3. Monsanto has stated that hundreds of studies have shown GBHs to be safe. It turns out that the published medical

literature contains hundreds of studies showing GBHs and the active ingredient, glyphosate, to be toxic. Furthermore, a large number of the studies showing it to be safe were performed by Monsanto or by researchers they hired. Many of these studies were not peer reviewed, nor published, and were done many years ago.

4. It is important to note that pharmaceutical and chemical companies often use their own studies to pass the first hurdles for approval, but at least in the world of medicine once a drug has been approved, physicians take the follow-up studies showing harm very seriously. In the case of pesticides, the EPA only re-reviews them every fifteen years and the chemical companies often minimize the concerns of ongoing studies.

3

GUT REACTION

*We have subjected enormous numbers of people to
contact with these poisons, without their consent and
often without their knowledge.*

—Rachel Carson, *Silent Spring (1962)*

During the years I served as a hospital CEO, we developed a sister relationship with a hospital for the poor in the Philippines. The hospital had warm, caring staff that worked unbelievably hard with almost no funding, taking care of the poorest of the poor. In the obstetric ward, there were four mothers and four babies for each post-delivery bed. Two mothers would sit on the floor or stand with their newborns while two mothers and their babies would use the bed. Then they would rotate.

Each time our team visited from our modern Hawaiian hospital, we would bring bags of donated medical supplies. On one of the trips, we walked as usual into the pediatric ward. It was a large room filled with ill children. Just inside the door, in a battered crib near the nurse's desk, was a very sick-looking little girl about eighteen months old. She was pale, on oxygen, and laboring for every breath. They told us that she had pneumonia, and despite receiving antibiotics, she was getting worse. They feared that she had staph pneumonia.

Staph pneumonia is an awful illness. The first sign is often that a child keeps getting sicker despite regular antibiotics, and when you do a chest X-ray there may be abscesses in their lungs.

Behind me, men were carrying in the bags of supplies that we had brought with us. The doctors asked if there was any chance that we had methicillin. This is a special antibiotic that can cure many staph infections. Fortunately, we had it. In minutes, they had the medicine running into the little girl's IV. Three days later we made rounds and found her playing in her crib and smiling. This is the kind of story that people who provide medical care in developing nations tell all the time, and we all feel good that our advanced medical systems can provide drugs that cure.

Embedded in this story, however, is an ever-present threat to everyone on the planet. The fear is of superbugs: bacteria or fungi that are resistant to all known treatments spreading across the globe. A note of clarification is needed here. The coronavirus pandemic sweeping the world at the time of the first printing of this book is a viral infection. The Center for Communicable Diseases (CDC) report below does not discuss treatments for viral diseases. This chapter is essentially about bacteria and fungi, not viruses.

The CDC published a report in November 2019 presenting data that deserved much more publicity than it received.[13] The CDC stated that previous studies had underestimated the number of infections (bacterial and fungal) resistant to our current antibiotics or antifungal medications. The new estimates are that each year there are 2.8 million cases of antibiotic-resistant infections in the United States, and that 35,000 Americans die annually as a result of these infections. This means that every eleven seconds a person in the United States gets an infection resistant to antibiotics and every fifteen minutes someone dies from one of these infections. The CDC began this document by stating that we must stop referring to a time in the future when antibiotics will not work well enough. They state that this time is "already here."

Resistant bacteria and fungi have the ability to make us all feel as if we are in a hospital for the indigent lacking the right medication—and visitors from more modern facilities will not be there to save us.

As mentioned earlier, glyphosate is patented as an antibiotic as well as an herbicide—a fact that is not well-known. Emerging studies show that its antibiotic effect on health may be much more profound than previously believed. Although the metabolic pathway that causes glyphosate to kill plants is not found in mammals, this pathway is present in many bacteria and fungi.

The microbiome is the name given to the bacteria that live in and on our bodies. The human body has somewhere between three and ten times as many bacteria as it does human cells. Reflect on this concept for a moment. To state it another way, most cells that make any one of us a unique individual are actually cells of bacteria in and on our body. It is estimated that the average human is coated inside and out with ten billion bacteria.

These bacteria are essential to our health. When they are friendly bacteria in a proper balance and properly diverse, they help digest our foods. These bacteria also aid in regulating neurotransmitters. They affect our mood, play a role in allergies, help prevent obesity and diabetes, and contribute to the proper functioning of our immune system. Dysfunction in the microbiome may cause inflammatory diseases such as ulcerative colitis and Crohn's disease. There is also increasing evidence that disturbances in the microbiome may play a role in autism, Parkinson's disease, and Alzheimer's.[14,15,16]

A fascinating and potentially landmark study from Arizona State University was published in April 2019.[17] This study followed eighteen children with the diagnoses of autism spectrum disease (ASD) and chronic gastrointestinal (GI) symptoms. The researchers had treated all these children with a fecal implant—meaning that they took stool from healthy donors and implanted it in the intestines of these children.

The results were dramatic. Testing of the treated children's intestinal microbiome after the transplant revealed a much more diverse and healthier set of bacteria inhabiting their intestines. Virtually all of their GI symptoms had disappeared or were dramatically improved.

Even more impressive was a 47 percent improvement in their autism scores. According to the researchers—using one of the most accurate autism scoring methods—83 percent of these children were rated as "severe" before treatment. Two years after treatment, only 17 percent were rated as severe; 39 percent were in the mild to moderate range; and most dramatic, 44 percent of the participants no longer met the autism criteria!

This study needs to be repeated with a non-treated control group, but these are exciting results. This type of improvement is uncommon in autism. It was mentioned that many of these infants had GI symptoms from birth, and it may be possible that their intestinal microbiomes were unhealthy from infancy.

A 2018 study by European researchers gives credibility to the idea that a pregnant mother's diet that includes glyphosate-containing foods could affect the intestinal bacteria of their infants.[18] In a rat study, pregnant rats were fed a diet containing glyphosate—most importantly, the amount of glyphosate was at a comparable level to that which is considered safe for humans. Even so, the baby rats had microbiome changes described by the researchers as "significant and distinctive" in comparison to the rat infants whose mothers were not exposed to glyphosate.

Another 2018 study done by researchers from a Moroccan university, this time in mice, showed that feeding mice glyphosate-containing diets resulted in measurable increases in anxiety and depression.[19] The amount of glyphosate fed to these mice was less than the proportional amount that is thought to cause adverse effects in humans, and again the changes to the microbiome were significant.

In November 2018, a study from the University of Minnesota[20] demonstrated that within months of arrival, the microbiome of immigrants from Southeast Asia changed to a pattern similar to that of the U.S. population—with a great loss of what appears to be healthy bacterial diversity. It is worth noting that other studies have shown that similar immigrant groups, after arriving in America, develop chronic diseases and conditions such as obesity and diabetes at much higher rates than are found in their native countries.

Why does the microbiome of these immigrants so rapidly lose its healthy diversity and become similar to the less diverse U.S. microbiome? During a follow-up interview, research scientists wondered if antibiotic exposure or the loss of fiber in the immigrants' new American diet played a role. Although the scientists' suggestions about the overuse of traditional antibiotics and loss of fiber could very well be part of the reason for this rapid change in the microbiome, studies suggest another hidden culprit: the antibiotic effect of GBHs sprayed on our food crops.

■ ■ ■

GBHs are the most heavily sprayed herbicides in the world. Over nine million tons of these chemical formulations have been sprayed worldwide since 1974. Glyphosate has found its way into the food supply of most of the developed world.

To repeat: the majority of the nonorganic American corn, soy, canola oil, sugar beets, and considerable amounts of our wheat, oats, and rice contain measurable amounts of glyphosate. It is even found in tampons and the clothes we wear, as GBHs are used in growing nonorganic cotton.

Three recent studies in New Zealand highlight evidence of GBHs' antibiotic properties and effect on bacteria. The first, published in 2015, showed that bacteria exposed to GBHs demonstrate increased resistance to antibiotics in laboratory settings.[21]

A second study was published in 2017, substantiating and clarifying these results.[22] The research appears to show that GBHs turn on a process in potentially harmful bacteria, which allows them to resist not one but multiple antibiotics. A third study published in 2018 showed "that when bacteria are simultaneously exposed to GBHs and traditional antibiotics, bacteria with higher levels of resistance can evolve. In some cases, resistance evolved 100,000 times faster."[23]

Several recent studies show that glyphosate alters the microbiome of honeybees, making the bees more susceptible to infection, less effective as pollinators, and less able to properly navigate.[24,25]

Previous studies have also shown that glyphosate adversely affects the intestinal bacteria in poultry and cattle.[26,27] Even the bacteria in exposed soil appear to be affected, as shown by studies on soil health done at the University of Missouri by a USDA scientist and others.[28, 29]

The growing evidence is that most of us have this herbicide and its metabolites in our bodies most of the time. A recent twenty-three-year study by the University of California-San Diego School of Medicine found that 70 percent of the patients followed had detectable levels of glyphosate or its metabolites in their urine by 2016, compared to a small number of this same group who had shown detectable levels in the 1990s.[30] An ongoing study of pregnant women in Indiana found that 90 percent had glyphosate in their urine.[31] A study in Germany involving two thousand people found that 99.6 percent had glyphosate in their urine. In 75 percent of those tested in this German study, the amount in their urine was at least five times greater than the amount allowed in drinking water.[32]

For physicians and our patients, it has become obvious that the overuse of antibiotics poses a severe threat to the health of individuals and populations. The risk includes, as mentioned, the genuine fear of superbugs with antibiotic resistance as well as adverse changes to our microbiome.

That our microbiome plays a significant role in maintaining health or causing ill health has become fully medically accepted. If our microbiomes are being disturbed by GBHs in our food, we must consider the ramifications, as well as the fact that the increase in chronic diseases in America runs parallel to the increase in GBH applications to our food supply.

Summary

1. **Glyphosate is patented as an antibiotic. Humans have more than ten billion bacteria in and on our bodies and they play substantial roles in the digestion of food, production of vital chemicals, protection against inflammation and infection, regulation of moods, and in multiple other processes vital for good health.**

2. **Increasing numbers of studies demonstrate that glyphosate interferes with the balance of bacteria in and on living bodies and that this alteration may promote the emergence of multiple chronic diseases and conditions, including the very worrisome possibility of broadening antibiotic resistance.**

3. **There are also studies showing that the large amount of glyphosate sprayed worldwide results in the populations of many countries having glyphosate in their bodies most of the time.**

4

THE STUDIES KEEP COMING

For the first time in the history of the world, every human being is now subjected to contact with dangerous chemicals, from the moment of conception until death.

—*Rachel Carson, Silent Spring (1962)*

The news and studies concerning the dangers of glyphosate/ Roundup/GBHs are appearing at an ever-increasing speed. When I started writing this book in early 2019, I had a general outline of the material I wanted to cover based on research findings. The problem is that the research on the dangers of glyphosate produces worrisome news on a regular basis. The two studies below were heavily publicized the week that I started this section. I decided to deviate from my outline and include them here as they are both important and possibly groundbreaking in their respective fields.

The study below was published in April 2019.[33] It is the first study of its particular type and provides a powerful clue to remarkable health dangers. The study looked at "transgenerational effects" of glyphosate exposure on pregnant rats. Transgenerational is a fancy way to describe effects passed down from generation to generation. In the study, pregnant rats had glyphosate added to their food for just six days. The dose they were exposed to was one half of the dosage that has been shown to cause adverse effects. The researchers then examined the mothers (called generation F0), their first-generation children (F1) and then the children of the children (F2) and then the children of those children (F3).

The results were startling and chilling. There were minimal adverse findings in the exposed mothers or the F1 generation offspring after this brief exposure. But there were marked abnormalities in the F2 and F3 generations (grandchildren and great-grandchildren). The latter two generations showed statistically significant and "dramatic" increases in obesity, kidney disease, ovarian disease, prostate disease, and birth abnormalities. These findings were associated with marked abnormalities in the DNA found in the sperm of the F1, F2, and F3 generations.

It has become well accepted that toxic exposures during pregnancy may affect the DNA in the sperm or eggs of the unborn. Once born, those children may go on to pass these DNA deformities to their offspring. Because it is affecting the DNA in the sperm or eggs of the developing fetus, the malformations are not seen until *the children of the children* are born. These are transgenerational and "epigenetic" changes. Epigenetic means the sequence of genes did not change, but the expression of those genes has changed.

Epigenetics is an exciting new chapter in the field of genetics because it is based on the knowledge that although we are stuck with the genes we are born with, we actually have some control in turning these genes off and on. It can also be a frightening field of study because it means that exposure to toxic substances or even toxic situations can turn genes on and off, and these changes may also be passed on for generations.

An example of epigenetics can be found in another experiment done with rats.[34] It has been demonstrated that mother rats who lick their pups have pups who grow up to be calmer adults. That makes sense, but it has also been shown that if you compare the offspring of the licked pups with the children of the un-licked pups, the licked pups' children are also calmer. This means that the second generation inherited calmer behaviors from the first generation. The process involved in this study is the turning on or off of specific genes that produce calming chemicals.

The obesity findings may provide a clue to the mystery of why this generation of Americans is so overweight. When I was young, people did not look like they do now, and the statistics are there to back up this perception of increasing obesity. Almost everyone in America now looks round with round faces, round bellies, rounded arms, and the number of really heavy people (morbidly obese) has skyrocketed.

In this rat study, a full 40 percent of the second- and third-generation offspring were obese. This was more than double the percentage of obesity seen in the offspring of the rats who were not exposed to glyphosate. Apparently, the Roundup exposure of the pregnant mothers affected the genes that control obesity, and this was passed on, transforming the grandchildren and great-grandchildren rats dramatically.

The second study that interrupted the planned flow of this book was published in 2019 by University of Washington (UW) researchers and deals with GBHs and cancer.[35] The most publicized aspects of the Roundup controversy have been the possibility of links between glyphosate and cancer. When a UN committee stated that glyphosate "probably" causes cancer, this sparked worldwide controversy, similar to the historical debate about whether smoking causes cancer. It now seems so obvious that smoking does cause lung cancer—how could it ever have been questioned?—but it certainly is still debated whether glyphosate causes cancer.

The UW researchers performed a meta-analysis of studies that addressed this question of a linkage between glyphosate and cancer. A meta-analysis is a review of multiple studies in order to better understand trends—as opposed to relying on a single study. The researchers were particularly interested in examining studies that included participants with heavy glyphosate exposure and in studies that followed the participants for long enough to allow the possible cancers to develop.

The multiple investigations they included in their analysis followed 65,000 people. A study they included for the first time in an analysis such as this was the 2018 update of the long-running Agricultural Health Study (AHS). The AHS has been following over 50,000 pesticide applicators in America since 1993. It was noted that the 2018 update of the information on these applicators showed a five-times increase in the cancer incidence for these applicators since the previous review in 2005.

The conclusion of this latest meta-analysis by UW (which included the 2018 update of the AHS study) is that there is an overall 41 percent increase in risk for non-Hodgkin's lymphoma (NHL) in applicators who had a high level of exposure to spraying or handling GBHs.

For science to accept the idea that one process causes another, there has to be a correlation in time *and* evidence from other studies supporting a mechanism for causation. This study by UW also examined the issue of whether animal and other studies supported the concept that glyphosate exposure could lead to an increase in the incidence of cancer. Studies have shown that lymphomas may be caused by an increase in inflammation, endocrine disruptions, oxidative stress, and damage to DNA. The researchers reviewed the animal, human, and mechanistic studies concerning glyphosate and these types of toxicities. They determined that there is ample evidence that glyphosate is toxic in all of the ways listed above and therefore potentially could act as a causative agent for NHL. The conclusion of their study was clearly stated:

> The overall evidence from human, animal, and mechanistic studies presented here supports a compelling link between exposures to GBHs* and increased risk for NHL.**

---

*GBHs: Glyphosate-based herbicides
**NHL: Non-Hodgkin's lymphoma

Summary

1. During the writing of this book, in early 2019, worrisome studies about glyphosate became a regular event.

2. A study demonstrated that brief exposures to doses considered nontoxic to pregnant rats was associated with abnormalities in the grandchildren and great-grandchildren of the pregnant rats. These generations showed statistically significant and "dramatic" increases in obesity, kidney disease, ovarian disease, prostate disease, and birth abnormalities. These findings were associated with marked abnormalities in the DNA found in the sperm of the F1, F2, and F3 generations.

3. A study by University of Washington researchers showed a 41 percent increase in risk of cancer in people who had heavy exposures to glyphosate-based formulations.

5

FATTY LIVERS

Is life worth living, it all depends on the liver.

—*William James*

My first hospital patient as a medical student was a man with hepatorenal syndrome. Up to that moment, most of medicine for me had been abstract, coming from books and instructors. Suddenly, in front of me was a man I was supposed to follow. He was thin, his skin and his eyes were yellow, and the first thing I learned was that he would die. At this point, however, he was quite alive and in his midfifties, but his liver had failed and then his kidneys. In those days, once both organ systems failed, death was almost inevitable. I remember poring over research, not willing to believe that there was no treatment that could save him. My efforts were in vain. The vision and sadness of his thin body in a hospital bed has stayed with me.

A study performed by researchers at the University of California-San Diego came out in May 2019 that may provide a particularly important clue as to why we are becoming sicker as a nation and as a world.[36] The California researchers followed patients with non-alcoholic fatty liver disease (NAFLD) and graded the severity of the damage to the liver. They also measured the amount of glyphosate and glyphosate metabolites in each patient's urine. They found that the higher the level of glyphosate and its metabolites were in the urine, the more severe the liver disease. The importance of this sentence needs to be fully understood.

Since glyphosate is eliminated from the body in the urine, the levels in the urine are thought to reflect how much glyphosate one has taken in. Glyphosate enters our bodies by the food we eat, the air we breathe, and the water we drink. This study suggests that those of us taking in more glyphosate and peeing more glyphosate out have a greater chance of having more severe liver disease.

Knowing how important this study's results are requires knowing more about fatty liver disease. It is estimated that 25–30 percent of American adults have NAFLD. That means 100 million Americans and possibly one billion people around the globe are affected by this condition. The disease incidence is also increasing rapidly. The percentage of Americans having it has almost doubled since just 2005, *and* most people who have this disease don't actually know they have it![37]

The disease is aptly named non-alcoholic fatty liver disease. These are livers of people who are not alcoholics, yet their livers are becoming filled with fat. Ten to 20 percent of people with this condition progress to a more severe condition called non-alcoholic steatohepatitis (NASH), and a percentage of these patients proceed to cirrhosis and cancer of the liver. Patients with fatty livers also suffer and die at a higher rate from cardiovascular disease and have a greater incidence of type 2 diabetes, obesity, and a measure of ill-health called metabolic syndrome. More and more studies are linking all of these medical conditions; each one may be caused by the other, and then each plays a role in worsening the other disease. Diabetes and obesity are associated with resistance to insulin, and it has been shown that as the liver gets sicker, it also plays a role in increasing resistance to insulin. Resistance to insulin makes diabetes, obesity, and liver disease worse. Bottom line: all of these diseases are part of a deadly circle leading to worsening health and premature death.[38]

Studies looking at common factors in patients with diabetes, obesity, and fatty liver disease have often laid the blame on poor diets—diets high in sugar-filled, processed foods. Processed foods are essentially any food that comes from a factory instead of a farm. It is the food that fills the shelves in the middle of grocery stores. It comes in boxes, cans, and various wrappings and has long ingredient lists.

Modern thinking has been that the high-sugar/low-nutrient quality of processed foods is the explanation for this global shift to ill health. This study, demonstrating higher levels of glyphosate in the urine in those with more severe liver disease, should act as a light bulb going on above all our heads. Processed foods, particularly in America, are heavily laced with glyphosate because so many of them contain GMO corn, GMO soy, GMO sugar beets, and may also contain grains such as wheat, rice, and oats that have been dried with glyphosate. To put it more strongly, this study suggests that the more glyphosate we consume, the sicker we get, at least in terms of liver disease. Increasing evidence shows that worsening fatty liver disease is associated with and probably plays a role in worsening other medical conditions such as diabetes, obesity, heart disease, and unfortunately much more.

This study just shows an association. As stated previously in this book and continuously repeated by the chemical companies, "An association does not prove causation." Or in other words, just because something is linked to something else does not prove that one caused the other.

For example, the glyphosate level could be higher with more severe fatty liver disease because these patients ate more processed food. If most processed food in America contains glyphosate, then one might have higher levels just because they are eating more of these foods, and it still could be the other additives and the extra sugar in these foods that are causing the obesity and fatty livers—not the glyphosate. It's analogous to being present at a crime but not actually being the person who committed the crime.

This is where animal studies become important. If you can take one group of rats or fish or other living entities and give that group glyphosate-containing foods or water to drink or swim in and another group an environment free of pesticides, you can follow the two groups and monitor their health—in this case, their liver health.

Scientists should be asking whether or not there is evidence, particularly animal study evidence, that links glyphosate to fatty livers (or that links glyphosate to the other forces that lead to fatty livers, such as inflammation, changes in the microflora, and increased insulin resistance).

Many published studies have clearly shown that exposure to glyphosate causes liver disease. In May 2019, Pubmed (the index to the National Library of Medicine) showed that in the prior ten years there had been 103 papers published on the subject of glyphosate and the liver. More than half (68) of these had been published in the prior five years.

Monsanto and the EPA claim that glyphosate is safe, but virtually every one of the papers published in that five-year period presented evidence of toxicity to the liver following exposure to glyphosate (or formulations containing glyphosate). In fact, only three studies in the five years indexed in the National Library of Medicine under the topics of "glyphosate and liver" presented evidence that might suggest that glyphosate is *not* toxic to the liver. Two of these papers that said there was no evidence of toxicity have an interesting twist. I will return to them after I briefly outline the various studies showing toxicity.

Thirty-two of the papers published in that five-year period are on the subject of the livers of fish and glyphosate. This is considered a critical topic, as fish are frequently exposed to the runoff of pesticides contaminating their watery environment. Concentrations of glyphosate used in these experiments ranged from the amount that is legal in drinking water to the amount that is often found in sprayed fields, to more substantial amounts that were usually not enough to kill a fish but higher than one would typically see in the environment. Once again, virtually none of these studies showed no toxic effect; even the study with the amount legal in drinking water showed significant biochemical effects.[39] The toxic effects ranged from increases in blood levels of common liver enzymes to DNA damage, to increased production of substances present in inflammation, to increased evidence of oxidation processes (oxidation in the body is somewhat similar to rust on your car) and/or evidence that the liver was trying to compensate for oxidative damage. Bottom line: even at environmentally accepted levels, glyphosate is toxic to the livers of fish!

So, one might say: fish are fish. They are not even mammals. Are the fish stories relevant to humans? The toxicity to fish and the overwhelming evidence that glyphosate is toxic to more than just plants is important, but studies in mammals are vital to understanding what may be happening in humans. The poor rat is the most commonly used lab animal helping us to understand what may be going on in humans.

Over that same five years, the National Library of Medicine indexed twenty studies covering the effect of glyphosate on rat livers. All but three of these studies showed glyphosate (or its commercial formulation) to be toxic to rat livers.

In the studies showing harm, seven of the studies administered glyphosate in a low dose, including doses proportionate in rats to those that are considered acceptable for human consumption. The rats on this low-dose diet were followed for various periods up to two years. The patterns of liver toxicity included damage to DNA and RNA, elevations of liver enzymes, liver cell destruction, disruptions of the usual patterns of protein and metabolic pathways, and (most importantly for this chapter) evidence that the damage is similar to the type of damage that can lead to fatty liver disease.[40] Ten of the studies used glyphosate doses higher than acceptable (again, proportionate for rats) for consumption, but not enough to kill the rats. These showed similar patterns of liver toxicity.

One of the low-dose studies was particularly important and should be alarming if one is not already alarmed.[41] It was the only study that compared and evaluated changes to the intestinal bacteria in rats that were exposed to glyphosate formulations and those that were not. This study showed not only evidence of liver toxicity but also evidence that the intestinal bacteria were altered. The ratios of certain important bacterial groups were changed, becoming similar to the ratios seen with obesity and fatty liver disease. This raises the possibility that glyphosate is not only directly toxic to the liver, but it may also be indirectly toxic by adversely altering intestinal bacteria.

This leads us to the studies that showed no harm. Two of these studies were particularly interesting to me. The first, which received a lot of press, was done by a group in France and reported no difference in health between rats fed for up to six months with formulas containing Roundup-ready GMO crops and those fed non-GMO crops.[42] The study appeared very sophisticated and analyzed multiple physical measures. What was not apparent in the summary of the article, but was described in the body of the paper, was that when they analyzed the food in both the non-GMO diets and the GMO diets, they each had the same amount of Roundup in them. The amount was actually so small in all the diets that they stated that they were not able to report on any Roundup effect. I also noticed that this was yet another study that sought input from "interested stakeholders," and in the first meeting of the interested stakeholders, all NGO representatives walked out and never returned, due to their concerns about chemical industry influence.

The second study was done by a group that has produced studies showing harm from Roundup in the past.[43] Similar to the above study, they also compared the health of rats on GMO and non-GMO diets, and they also saw no significant health differences despite very sophisticated testing. They also tested the food in the GMO and non-GMO groups for the presence of glyphosate, and they found no glyphosate in any of the food being fed to the rats. They hypothesized that this GMO food may have only been sprayed by Roundup once, early in its growth, and therefore had minimal to no amount present at the time of harvest.

The reason both of these studies are of interest is that they *don't* demonstrate that Roundup in our food is safe. They just show that different rat food formulas have varying amounts of Roundup in them, and if we want to determine whether Roundup in the diet harms or does not harm rats or humans, we have to be sure there is Roundup in the test diets.

The third study showing no harm was more straightforward.[44] It was a review of cancer studies and concluded that there was no evidence that glyphosate causes liver cancer in rodents. It was one of the many studies designed to weigh in on the international debate about glyphosate and cancer. This question about glyphosate causing cancer has led to battles in courtrooms, regulatory agencies, and the media. I will return to this topic in another chapter.

Summary

1. **For the first time, a human study showed that for patients with non-alcoholic fatty liver disease, the more glyphosate in their urine, the worse the disease. This study is in addition to a large number of studies showing glyphosate to be toxic to the livers of fish and rats.**

2. **Non-alcoholic fatty liver disease is a rapidly growing worldwide epidemic. This fatty liver condition is not only dangerous in itself but plays a role in the worsening of diabetes, obesity, heart disease, and other medical conditions.**

3. Numerous studies have blamed our increasing ill health on the high sugar, additive-filled, low nutritional quality of processed foods.

4. Much less thought has been given to the fact that another substance found in processed foods is glyphosate and that there is growing evidence that this chemical may be exacerbating all the other disease-causing properties of processed foods. It is time for us to seriously consider that this may be the case.

6

OBESITY

*We are spending millions, if not billions of dollars every year
on programs to fight the childhood obesity epidemic while
giving almost $2 billion of taxpayer money to the junk food
and fast food industries to make the epidemic worse.*

—Dennis Kucinich

About ten years ago, my wife and I visited Vietnam. Having
been a student during the Vietnam War, I was well aware
of the scars and horror suffered both by the Vietnamese
and by our American soldiers. We traveled there with some trepi-
dation, fearing that they would hate us for being Americans.

Instead we found, much to our relief and pleasure, a country of
very friendly people who genuinely seemed to like Americans. We
also found a country with inexpensive, fresh, real food, hot soups
full of vegetables and a healthy-appearing population with almost
no sign of obesity or malnutrition.

One of the magical sights was the daily occurrence of thousands of children riding their bikes to school. Most memorable,
and often noted by travel writers, was the scene of high school girls
riding their bikes in a uniform of long white pants and flowing
white tops, sitting very erect with black hair cascading down their

backs. They have been described as swans riding bicycles. And striking to a Westerner, virtually none of these children showed any sign of being overweight.

The contrast of these Vietnamese to the crowds of overweight and often obese American and European tourists was striking. Frequently we would be in conversation with friendly, very trim Vietnamese men or women and they would bring out photos of relatives living in America. In virtually all of these pictures, the relatives who had moved to America were now overweight. One could see the familial similarities, but the weight gain in a single generation of living in America was always striking and depressing and should be part of a wake-up call for the Western world.

The evidence is getting stronger by the day. We are not fat because it is our genetic destiny. We are heavy because of what we eat and, to a much lesser degree, by a decrease in activity. It is not dramatic to say that obesity has become one of the deadliest epidemics in the history of the world—made even more frightening by the fact that obesity rates are increasing almost everywhere.

Before I jump into the evidence for the main drivers of the obesity epidemic, I want to make one more effort to drive home the point that something in the last fifty years and perhaps more so in the past twenty-five years has made Westerners and everyone who has adopted our diet look very different. The statistics are available to back up the visual perceptions, but often visuals can act as a stronger prompt than tables of numbers.

When I was young, in the 1950s and 1960s, people did not look like they do now. People were essentially thin. If you look at photos of graduating classes, particularly in the early part of the 1900s, virtually everyone in the picture is thin by today's standards. One rarely saw a massively obese person. As people neared middle age, they gained some weight around their middle, but the massively protuberant bellies, round arms, and round faces we currently see everywhere were almost nonexistent, except for pregnant women or heavy beer drinkers. Now we almost look like a different race.

This chapter on obesity is divided into two sections. The first is about the possible role that glyphosate is playing in the obesity epidemic. The second part is about the compelling evidence that ultra-processed food—food that we export around the world—is the primary driver of the massive weight gain in most developed nations. Although glyphosate may have some role in the adverse effect of this ultra-processed "fake food," it is not the only ingredient causing the problems.

Michael Pollan is one of the foremost authors in the world on the subject of food. He wrote an op-ed in the *New York Times* in 2009.[45] Although at the time, Obama was doing his best to try and fix our broken healthcare system in America, Pollan felt the president was not addressing the "elephant in the room." That elephant in the room (perhaps an intentional pun) is that Americans are paying more than double per person for healthcare than Europeans. Pollan goes on to state that a substantial portion of that increase in cost is because as a nation, we are also much more overweight than our European counterparts. He states that we are spending $2.3 trillion for healthcare and that three-quarters of that amount is used to treat "preventable chronic" diseases and "many if not most" of these diseases are linked to diet. He states:

> We're spending $147 billion to treat obesity, $16 billion to treat diabetes, and hundreds of billions more to treat cardiovascular disease and the many types of cancer that have been linked to the so-called Western diet. One recent study estimated that 30% of the increase in healthcare spending over the past 20 years could be attributed to the soaring rate of obesity, a condition that now accounts for nearly a tenth of all spending on health care.

Those numbers were 2009 numbers. The U.S. numbers in 2019 are $3.7 trillion for healthcare and $310 billion of that is used for obesity. Those numbers, although large, do not come close to describing the personal misery caused by ill health in our population. To restate, one in two American adults is said to have a chronic disease. For the first time in modern history, our life expectancy is going down. Many of us wake up every morning not only *not* wanting to look at our layers of fat in the mirror but also dealing on a daily basis with medication costs, medication side effects, and the general lousy feeling of spending at least the last twenty to thirty years of our lives not feeling well.

Obesity and Glyphosate

There is powerful and growing evidence that our ultra-processed food is playing a significant role in causing obesity and ill health. There is also a growing suspicion that glyphosate in our food supply may be an additional cause of obesity. The graphs by Swanson and others shown in Chapter 1 show an increase in the incidence of obesity and diabetes that match the rapid increase in the use of glyphosate in our food supply. As mentioned, though, an association is not proof of causation.

The previous chapters described, that despite Monsanto's constant reminders that hundreds of studies have shown glyphosate to be safe, there are hundreds of studies which demonstrate that glyphosate is toxic. In April 2019, if one searched the National Library of Medicine online site for glyphosate and obesity, there were only four articles referenced which even discuss the possibility of a connection. A person's first thought might well be that Monsanto and their supporters could be right: there is minimal evidence that glyphosate-containing formulations cause obesity.

I believe, however, that despite the absence of overwhelming proof that it causes obesity, the possible connection will increasingly be the subject of scientific research. The reasons include the following:

1. There is increasing and compelling evidence that alterations to the microbiome (the bacteria in and on our bodies) play a role in the promotion of obesity.

2. There is also ever-increasing evidence that glyphosate and formulations containing glyphosate can and do cause alterations in the microbiome of many species. (See Chapter 3.)
3. Therefore, there is at least the possibility that glyphosate's ability to cause changes in the microbiome may also play a role in causing obesity.

Those three statements prove nothing; they merely suggest a possibility. Still, it is important to note that the few studies that have attempted to look at this specific possibility are very suggestive that there may be a real connection.

Before I go to the studies concerning glyphosate and obesity, I want to review the growing belief that alterations to the microbiome play a role in unintended weight gain.

In May 2019, the National Library of Medicine listed 3,865 articles concerning research on obesity and the microbiome; 3,071 of these articles were published in the prior five years, and one-third of those were published in just the prior eighteen months. This explosion in interest and research is driven by the increasing understanding that our microbiome is extraordinarily vital in terms of human health. Fortunately, the tools used to examine the microbiome are also dramatically improving, allowing us to rapidly increase our research and knowledge.

The human intestinal tract is a genuinely miraculous creation. If you were to open it up and lay it out like a blanket, smoothing out the thousands of tiny villi (outpouchings), and other folded surfaces, the intestinal tract of a single adult could cover an entire football field. More surprising than its size is that when entirely laid out, it would have a thickness of less than a single sheet of very thin paper. This thin layer acts as a barrier and a filter. On one side of this fragile barrier is the food we eat, digestive enzymes produced by our body, and billions of bacteria. On the other side of this barrier are blood vessels that carry digested food materials to the cells in the body. This layer is so sophisticated that it allows the breakdown products of food to go through it and into our bloodstream while at the same time keeping billions of bacteria out of our blood and safely in the intestines.

I grew up in a very old house. The kids in the neighborhood, in the kind fashion that kids often have, would say that our home was held up by the termites holding hands. In the same way that termites holding hands may have protected our home, the GI tract is protected and enabled by the inter-relationships of the bacteria that inhabit it.

This thin layer of cells with its protective coating is teeming with life; billions of bacteria cover its entirety. They are active, interrelating, and producing chemicals that affect almost all the functions associated with keeping a body alive. The bacteria serve to strengthen and protect this tissue paper-thin layer. They help digest food, make vitamins, make substances that regulate the body's bacterial balance, fight infection, protect against inflammation, make us depressed or happy, and on and on. When they are diverse and in proper balance, we are usually healthy. If they are not in proper balance, we are unhealthy. Their balance and diversity depend to a large extent on what we eat and on the environmental chemicals we are exposed to.

This bacterial balance evolved over millions of years. The bacteria depend on us to eat the foods that they need to survive. They need fiber and nutritious substances. In the last hundred years, our microbiome has been exposed to an enormous shock. The shock is a diet never before seen in history: a diet of factory created foods—foods designed never to spoil; filled with additives; processed in plastic pipes; often containing hormones, antibiotics, emulsifiers; lacking fiber, and unfortunately often containing pesticides which are designed to be toxic to living organisms. And even more unfortunately, glyphosate is the most common of these pesticides, which, as mentioned, is actually patented as an antibiotic. Living up to its patent, it selectively kills bacteria—meaning that it allows certain bacteria to flourish while others die off.

The three thousand-plus studies concerning the microbiome and obesity are opening the door to an immense store of knowledge, but we already are seeing patterns. These intestinal bacteria fall into broad general categories, much like the different groupings of people that make up the workforce of a country. There are two broad categories or phyla whose balance appears to be very important for good health. We now know that altering the ratio of these two types of bacteria may lead to obesity and toxicity to different organs, particularly the liver. Specifically, when the Firmicutes phyla changes in relation to the Bacteroidetes phyla, there is an increased risk of obesity and nonalcoholic liver disease.

In 2017, a study was published that examined these ratios.[46] Rats were exposed over two years to different concentrations of Roundup in their drinking water. The concentrations ranged from 0.1ppb (that is parts per billion) to 5000 ppm (parts per million). To give you an idea of what a part per billion is, if you put a pinch of salt in ten tons of potato chips, that would be equivalent to one part per billion, and this dose was one-tenth of that pinch of salt. One part per million would be the same as putting a drop of ink in a 55-gallon drum of water. To put this in another perspective, the EPA allows our food to contain up to 300 ppm of glyphosate (depending on the type of food product).

When they analyzed the rats' poop and organs after exposure to these minimal amounts of glyphosate in drinking water, female rats were found to have their microbiome ratios altered in a fashion that has been associated with obesity. When the scientists looked at the female rat livers, they also discovered evidence of liver disease. In other words, amounts of glyphosate, at levels that are probably much less than we are regularly exposed to, altered the microbiome of female rats in dangerous ways. The scientists suggest that this effect on female rats and not male rats indicated that at these low doses, there is also a hormonal effect that has more do with women's hormones than men's. That is not reassuring; it provides further evidence that Roundup affects our hormones as well as our bacteria.

The Ramazzini Institute in Italy performed a similar study using pregnant rats.[47] They fed the expectant mothers a daily amount of glyphosate that matched, for rats, the amount allowable in the United States for human food. They fed it to the rats while they were pregnant and then while they were breastfeeding. They also analyzed their poop. In the poop of these baby rats, they observed the worrisome changes to the Firmicutes/Bacteroidetes ratios that have been associated with obesity.

Another piece of evidence possibly connecting glyphosate with obesity was the multigenerational study we reviewed in Chapter 4.[48] In this study, pregnant female rats were given glyphosate for six days, again in drinking water. The amount was one half of the amount considered to show no adverse effect and just about double what is acceptable as an industry-allowable amount. The researchers carefully followed the children and grandchildren and great-grandchildren of these pregnant rats to see what this glyphosate exposure did to the unborn. These types of studies are significant as the unborn fetuses are extremely susceptible to injury while they are developing their brains and organs. Small doses of toxins can have terribly negative effects on an infant, be it a rat or a human. By looking at the grandchildren and great-grandchildren, they were also looking at effects glyphosate may have on the sperm and egg of unborn fetuses. An effect on the sperm or egg only shows up in the grandchildren and the great-grandchildren of the fetuses exposed when their mothers were pregnant. The grandchildren and great-grandchildren were found to have a doubling and even a tripling of the rate of obesity over the rats that were not exposed. An analysis of sperm in the offspring showed marked abnormalities of gene expression.

The final study of the works we are reviewing here was an overall review of studies examining multiple chemicals and their possible roles in causing metabolic syndrome.[49] Metabolic syndrome has different definitions, but in general terms, it describes a condition of being overweight with abnormal lipids and abnormalities in how someone processes sugar. It is the medical condition that describes a large number of chronically ill people in today's world. This review included a review of glyphosate and described how studies show that even at low doses it can adversely affect the liver and kidneys, that it interrupts the process for making fat cells better able to handle fat, decreases the production of helpful chemicals, and increases the production of harmful substances from these same fat cells. They concluded that the sum of this research was worrisome enough to call for more studies on glyphosate and the metabolic syndrome.

Obesity, Ill-Health, and Ultra-Processed Foods

I finished my pediatric residency in Maine, and my wife and I were looking for an interesting place to start my practice of medicine. We had two small children and thought we would love to go somewhere unusual before we came back to Maine and joined an established pediatric practice. Guam is an island six hours west of Hawai'i by plane, and they were looking for pediatricians. Even though a super typhoon had hit Guam just months before with winds of 180 miles an hour, we bundled up our little family and moved out of New England. We traded Maine's stark beauty and cold ocean for an ocean that felt like a warm bath, and a verdant island surrounded by reefs and emerald lagoons.

Even when we first boarded the plane that flew from Honolulu to Guam, we knew we were entering a different world. Strong-looking men and large women dressed in clothes from the different Pacific islands got on the plane with us. We went to Guam on a contract for eighteen months and ended up staying for two-and-one-half years. We could not get over the lack of winter, the island lifestyle, the blending of multiple cultures, and the warm ocean.

A special part of our time there came from a friendship my wife had with a group of Tahitian dancers. In those days, the hotels on Guam were small and funky, and this troupe of eight Tahitians was the main show in one of the hotels. We spent magical evenings with them at the beach. The Tahitians would dive in the lagoon and catch fish, which they would then cook. We sat and ate under the stars, feeling the warm tropical night air with the constant background noise of the surf on the outside reef. The kids would run around, and the Tahitians would play their guitars. All of them were true athletes, in great shape, big, but not overweight. The men were powerfully built and the women graceful and full-bodied.

These Tahitians looked much like Pacific Islanders have looked for thousands of years. The story of what has happened to these peoples of the Pacific Islands is well documented in a 2006 paper entitled "Overweight in the Pacific: Links Between Foreign Dependence, Global Food Trade, and Obesity in the Federated States of Micronesia."[50]

The paper pointed out that the inhabitants of these Pacific islands were described by the first Western explorers such as Magellan as "singularly tall, muscular, and well-proportioned people." A French explorer stated, "I never saw men better made." Now, in 2019, the district of Kosrae, in the Federated States of Micronesia, has the most obese population on the globe. Here, 88 percent of the adult population is overweight, 59 percent are obese, and 24 percent are extremely obese. This population has been well studied. It has been shown that they share a genetic disposition towards obesity, but it only manifests if they depart from their traditional diet. The obesity epidemic happened quite rapidly once the United States took over the islands after World War II. In exchange for its militarily strategic position, we brought in aid, which meant money, and we brought our processed foods, which then could be easily bought with that new money.

The timing of the obesity epidemic has been well established, as the U.S. Navy had done a study of the population of Kosrae after World War II. At that time, there was a complete absence of obesity, hypertension, or diabetes. Starting in the 1960s, the cheap food and the financial aid—in terms of first millions, then billions of dollars—completely changed the diet and lifestyles of the Micronesians in Kosrae. They went from food self-sufficiency—eating fish, taro, breadfruit, coconuts, and bananas—to eating mostly store-bought, highly processed foods. Their new diet included foods with high fat such as SPAM, sweetened beverages, and sugar-laden foods of all types. The result was a perfect storm for obesity and ill-health. Their genetic makeup was unprepared for an onslaught of high fat, high sugar, processed foods, and they became less active because they were buying their food rather than fishing and farming.

Genes, processed foods, and less activity created a recipe for a health disaster with obesity, diabetes, and all of the associated illnesses sweeping through their islands. Food industry supporters and others have often placed most of the blame on genetics and less activity. Less activity certainly plays a role, but it is essential to understand that there was no genetic problem when these populations ate healthy non-processed foods. Our factory-created food is bad for everybody and appears to be particularly bad for populations that have been exposed to them over relatively short periods of history. The rapid onset of obesity, diabetes, and the rest of modern man's illnesses have been well documented in groups of Pima Indians, Samoans, other Polynesian populations, and almost everywhere it has been studied. When a group with similar genetics remains on their traditional diet, they remain non-obese and free of diabetes; and when they convert to the West's processed food diets, they rapidly manifest all the illnesses plaguing developed nations.

The evidence from Kosrae seems clear. Their population's change in diet has been well documented, and the simultaneous worsening of health and astounding increase in obesity is so closely linked in time that it seems hard *not* to conclude that this new diet caused their ill health. But one study is never enough to be completely convincing, and the manufacturers of ultra-processed foods are pushing back hard against the concept that their highly profitable food products cause health problems. So, are there other well-done studies showing the role that highly processed foods play in generating ill health?

The answer is yes. Several have been published just recently. In France, 105,159 adults participated in a study called the NutriNet-Santé study.[51] Their diets were exhaustively analyzed, and they were put in groupings dependent on their food preferences. The researchers were particularly interested in the group that ate the highest percentage of ultra-processed foods. These foods were described as mass-produced foods made in factories. They included mass-produced bread, pastries, packaged dried noodle meals, instant frozen or shelf-stable meals, processed meats such as bologna and salamis, chicken and fish nuggets, and similar foods. It was noted that the industrial processes used to make many of these foods use numerous food additives, including flavoring agents, colors, emulsifiers, and the like. These are the foods found filling the center of most American grocery stores. They are made in factories, and they do not look like real foods. In other words, they don't look like fruits, vegetables, unprocessed meats, or grains such as rice.

French studies on the health of these people have been ongoing since 2009. One study reported on cardiovascular and cerebrovascular health.[52] These groups were followed for 5.2 years. They found that for each 10 percent increase in ultra-processed food in the diet, there was an 11-13 percent increase in the number of people having evidence of cardiovascular or cerebrovascular diseases, including heart attacks and strokes.

Another study of this same group looked at the risk of cancer in general and breast cancer, specifically, in the group eating the most ultra-processed foods.[53] They demonstrated that for each 10 percent increase in ultra-processed foods, there was a 10 percent

increase in the risk of all cancer—and breast cancer, specifically.
A different study on a subset of this same population showed an
increase in irritable bowel symptoms with an increase in ultra-processed foods.

In Spain, a similar type of study (known as the SUN study)
followed university graduates, analyzed their diets, and followed
them closely.

1. One study followed close to 20,000 Spanish University graduates from 1999 to 2014.[54] They found that in the group
   that ate four or more servings of ultra-processed food per
   day there was a 62 percent increase in mortality from all
   causes. For each extra serving one had of these ultra-processed foods there was an 18 percent increase in all-cause
   mortality. All-cause mortality means one's chances of dying
   from anything.
2. Another study of Spanish graduates followed 8,451 subjects
   for close to nine years.[55] Those eating the highest amount
   of ultra-processed foods had a 26 percent increase in the
   probability of being obese. None of these participants were
   obese at the start of the study.
3. A third study of the university graduates followed close
   to 19,000 subjects for nine years and showed a 26 percent
   increase in the probability of developing hypertension in
   those on a high ultra-processed food diet.[56] Again, none of
   these participants had hypertension at the start.

In the United States, a similar study followed close to 12,000 adults
over nineteen years and found an increase in all-cause mortality of
31 percent in those with a higher intake of ultra-processed foods.[57]

These recent studies are compelling. The more factory-pro-
duced, ultra-processed food one eats, the higher the chance of
obesity, heart disease, stroke, hypertension, cancer and of just
dying sooner.

We must then ask, what is it about these ultra-processed foods that is causing the ill-health? There are many suspects, including the emulsifiers, the food additives, the plastics in the food containers, the altered fats, the high fats, and the high sugar content. There is also the chilling fact that thousands of substances allowed in our foods have never been fully tested. There is one concept, though, that may be more important than any single chemical.

When I was in medical school, they taught us that you get fat because you take in more calories than you burn up. The convenient thing about this explanation is it makes it easy to blame the overweight person. You ate more than you exercised off, so you are to blame. It is increasingly clear that not all calories are created equal, and different substances are really messing up how we digest and react to food. If we eat too much sugar, which we all do if we eat a processed food diet, the extra sugar not only provides an excess of calories, but the fructose part of the sugar molecule overwhelms our liver. That sugar rapidly and directly turns into fat and into substances that increase inflammation. It is then deposited in and around your liver. Inflammation itself also leads to obesity and ill-health.

In addition, foods containing antibiotics or having antibiotic properties (such as glyphosate) may alter our microbiome. And as the ratios of bacteria change, we run the risk of obesity, liver disease, depression, and more. Other food additives may alter the way our hormones work, and that can also affect weight and health.

It is not as simple as overeating. It is eating too much of ticking time bombs that make it almost impossible to eat American processed food and not become overweight, obese, or even massively obese.

Summary

1. **The worldwide obesity epidemic may well be one of the deadliest epidemics in history and is undoubtedly one of the most expensive. America spends in excess of $300 billion annually on obesity-related problems.**

2. There is substantial evidence that glyphosate-containing formulations affect the microbiome, and there is overwhelming evidence that alterations in the microbiome lead to many
health problems including obesity. An important and still
unanswered question is whether the effect of GBHs on the
microbiome is also one of the drivers of excess weight gain.

3. There is compelling evidence that glyphosate fed to pregnant
rats can affect multiple generations of offspring, and one
of the effects noticed was a doubling and tripling of obesity
rates in the offspring.

4. A review of studies shows that glyphosate adversely affects
lipids, the storage of fat, and the regulation of glucose.

5. Ultra-processed foods, meaning foods made in factories, usually with many ingredients, dramatically increase our odds
of having multiple medical conditions, including obesity, vas-
cular disease, cancer, and ultimately dying sooner than we
should. A high intake of processed foods could be as little as
only four servings a day.

7

HAWAIIAN GREEN SEA TURTLES, AND OCEAN LIFE AS WE KNOW IT

*Protection of Wildlife, Fish, Crustacea and
Environment. This product is highly toxic to aquatic
invertebrates. Do not contaminate dam, river or
stream with this product.*

—Monsanto label for Roundup

A little-known and simple adventure on the island of Kaua'i is viewing sea turtles as they come upstream to sleep. On the South Shore of Kaua'i, there is a place called Koloa Landing. You should arrive as the sun is setting. Park near the water. After walking a short distance over sharp lava rocks, you will arrive at a stream that runs inland.

As you settle in among the rocks, you soon realize that something dramatic is happening. Little dark objects that looked like floating coconuts come into better focus. This is not floating debris but the heads of dozens of giant Hawaiian green sea turtles. They look around with their ancient, hooded reptilian eyes, and gradually you see their large, shell covered bodies. And they keep coming, one after another: first, gracefully swimming, and then with much less grace but great determination pulling themselves up on

LEE A. EVSLIN, M.D.

the rock-strewn edges of the stream. They have come to sleep and probably to avoid having their sleeping bodies become a dinner for sharks cruising offshore. Another thing that you may notice if they swim close to you is that many of these regal creatures appear to have numerous small tumors on their heads, necks and other soft tissues.

I don't know what is causing these tumors. What is known though is that this particular stream runs by golf courses, and golf courses use atrazine and glyphosate to keep the grass uniform. There has been interest by marine scientists in exploring a connection between the tumors and environmental toxins, but as far as I know there has been no study showing a connection to pesticides. An investigation was done, however, on these beautiful sea creatures which should have gotten more publicity, particularly in a state like Hawai'i where the ocean is part of our soul.[58]

The Hawaiian green sea turtle is an endangered species. Killing one is a federal offense. This study did involve killing eight of them, but a federal agency sanctioned ending their lives. None of the eight were considered viable. The euthanasia was to eliminate a slower but certain death. Immediately after death, the researchers took cultures of the bacteria in the turtle intestines. They streaked the swabs on a special culture medium and then placed disks containing different concentrations of Roundup on the medium. They used concentrations of glyphosate similar to those found in the sea near European coastal communities. The disks of glyphosate "significantly" inhibited the growth of four types of bacteria taken from the digestive tracts of these turtles. This means that glyphosate at the levels found in coastal waters can significantly alter the sea turtles' intestinal microbiome. These bacteria are necessary for the turtles to digest food and for their general health. Researchers also mentioned that because glyphosate is an herbicide, it may affect the nutritive quality of the local seaweed, the main component of a turtle's diet.

Monsanto repeatedly reassured us that glyphosate is safe because it affects a metabolic pathway found in plants and not mammals. Yet again we see that glyphosate significantly affects the bacteria that inhabit all life-forms and are necessary for healthy living. As I tried to put glyphosate into perspective for our island state, I sought out what else had been discovered about glyphosate and aquatic life. Once again, the closer I looked, the more concerned I became.

Recent studies weave a compelling case that glyphosate is toxic to our oceans and waterways. Rain causes pesticides and fertilizers to run off the land into streams and drainage systems. Many of these, particularly in a small island state like Hawai'i, lead straight into the ocean. Numerous aquatic life forms have been tested against glyphosate, and the majority of published studies show toxicity. Several recent studies though are particularly concerning.

I have never gone diving on the Great Barrier Reef in Australia, but I have gone diving in the island nation of Palau. It was one of my life's peak experiences. The Marianas Trench runs right through that island nation. It is miles deep. When you dive, guides often take you to locations formed by the wall of the trench. If you dive down just fifteen to thirty feet and stay in one spot and look around for all the time your dive tanks allow you, you still cannot see all that it is possible to see. The coral walls of this trench are so full of beauty and life that one cannot come close to taking it all in. Not only do you see the seemingly limitless variations of coral and the fish swimming in and around the coral, but deep below huge, dark, blurry shapes glide by. These are huge groupers, sharks, rays, and all else that thrive in the trench.

The Great Barrier Reef in Australia is described in similarly glowing terms. It is the world's most extensive coral reef system, composed of over 2,900 individual reefs and 900 islands. It covers 133,000 square miles and stretches 1,400 miles.

The recent news is that it is dying. It is bleaching, meaning the coral is turning white and much of it may be too far gone to recover. Experts blame the bleaching on climate change, a warming ocean, cyclones, and pollution. In the hundreds of articles discussing the sad evidence of the illness of this reef system, there are a small number of studies that point to one particular stressor possibly having an outsized effect. There are also a growing number of environmentalists and scientists who are starting to be more outspoken about this possible connection.

In May 2018, researchers published a study from Vietnam.[59] They took coral from two locations in a beautiful Vietnamese bay. One place was a protected pristine area, and the other was more polluted by river runoff and nearby fish farms. They exposed the coral specimens to two different temperature waters and differing concentrations of glyphosate. They found the following:

1. The coral from the pristine area was more sensitive to all stressors.
2. The coral from the more polluted area showed minimal change when exposed to warmer water or to glyphosate alone.
3. All the coral had a significant increase in bleaching when exposed to the combination of the herbicide and the warmed water.

The conclusion was that combinations of stressors (in this case, a warming ocean and glyphosate) makes the damage to coral more extensive. The other point from the study is that coral health is dependent on the amount of specific plankton in their environment. The plankton acts as their food supply. Color changes measured in this study were described as being indicative of loss of this plankton, meaning a loss of nutrition for the coral.

Recent studies and satellite imagery combine to strengthen the evidence that glyphosate may be a contributor to the coral demise. Satellite imagery shows vast plumes of runoff stretching from river mouths to the Great Barrier Reefs after heavy rains. This runoff contains fertilizers and pesticides. The heavily soil-laden watery plumes decrease light getting down to the coral. And that amount of light getting down to the coral may also be important.

Another recent study was done with water taken from the Great Barrier Reef lagoon.[60] Scientists found that the half-life of glyphosate (the time it takes for one half of the glyphosate to degrade) in this seawater was 47 days under lowlight conditions and 315 days in the dark. Their study was the first of its kind to show the persistence of glyphosate in seawater. They pointed out that there is very little monitoring of glyphosate's presence offshore anywhere in the world and that the long half-life and potential to damage the reef is increased by the fact that glyphosate binds to soil. Therefore, it may be carried long distances and still be able to have adverse effects on life-forms.

The study from Vietnam, showing a decrease in plankton available for nutrition after exposure to glyphosate, is not alone in concluding that glyphosate-containing formulations affect plankton. In the chapter on obesity, we discussed the bacteria that cover the human intestinal tract by the billions. They are vital to the well-being of all living organisms. Further, their power lies in their numbers and in their relationship to each other.

In puddles, streams, ponds, lakes, and oceans, bacteria are also vital. But they are only part of a much more complex world of floating life-forms known as plankton. Plankton are the building blocks of life in the water. They are the life-forms that drift with the currents rather than swim on their own. All life in the seas and lakes depend on plankton for either their own nutrition or the nutrition of something they eat. Plankton are classified in broad categories. There are the plankton that are plant-like and use the sun for energy; these are phytoplankton. There are plankton that are small animals or immature forms of larger animals; these are known as zooplankton. As with the human microbiome, this biome of the sea is the healthiest when it is in balance. Out-of-balance plankton systems lead to unhealthy bodies of water and poor health for the plants, coral, amphibians, and fish that live in the oceans.

All of this brings us back to Hawai'i. There was a proposal to use a glyphosate formulation that is considered less toxic to waterways. They were going to use it adjacent to a beautiful body of ocean-linked pools in the town of Hilo on the Big Island. These pools are connected directly and indirectly to the sea by underground waterways. They are affected by the tides, full of life, and very popular with visitors and locals. The idea was to control weed growth near the ponds. Researchers from the University of Hawai'i (UH) were asked to investigate the potential for harm of spraying in the vicinity of these pools.[61] They took six specimens of macroalgae and seagrasses from these ponds and exposed them in the lab to concentrations of the glyphosate formulation that were less than the proposed levels for spraying. After exposure, they found profound adverse changes to the macroalgae and seagrasses. The algae and seagrasses responded less well to sunlight and produced less chlorophyll, signifying ill-health. The researchers "strongly" recommended that this glyphosate formulation *not* be used near these ponds.

The argument for using this particular formulation of the herbicide near the ponds was based on the manufacturer's description of it being safe near waterways as it breaks down quickly in soil and degrades in only a few days. In the report by UH, the researchers reviewed in detail studies showing that the glyphosate breakdown can take up to a year, depending on conditions. There is ample evidence that toxins will run off the land into the water, particularly during storms. Scientists also cited studies showing that glyphosate sprayed on land has been found in nearby shore locations, having adverse effects on organisms there.

The researchers also brought the discussion back to the Hawaiian green sea turtles which began this chapter. The green turtles are the largest marine herbivores in the Hawaiian Islands. Their diet consists of macroalgae and seagrasses. One of the seagrasses tested and found to have adverse responses to glyphosate is one of the grasses that these sea turtles eat.

To put all of this in perspective and to show that these are not just isolated studies, a review in the National Library of Medicine (NLM) paints a similar picture of the potential for harm from glyphosate formulations in bodies of water. In an analysis completed in June 2019, I searched the NLM for all studies referencing plankton and glyphosate; there were twenty-six studies referenced; virtually *all* of them showed adverse changes to plankton from exposures of glyphosate or glyphosate formulations. Two did go on to say that the overall effect would be minimal, but they nevertheless showed adverse effects.

Searching the NLM for glyphosate and fish revealed 194 studies. I reviewed each of the studies going back to January 2017. There were fifty studies from that date forward that examined the effect of glyphosate on fish. Again, virtually *all* of them showed toxicity. Concentrations in the experiments ranged from very low concentrations, which are completely legal in bodies of water, to higher concentrations. Designed to see what the effects are, every one of these studies showed toxic effects on the fish, their eggs, or their larvae. Only one study showed that although there was evidence of harm to fish, they appeared to be able to recover.

The harm shown to these fish or their offspring included the following:

- cell injury and death; particular cell lines were affected, including liver, gills kidneys, brains, as well as damage to the nucleus and the mitochondria of the cells[62,63,64]
- genetic damage to the fish and their embryos, sperm, and eggs[65]
- behavioral changes in the fish that made it more difficult for them to escape predators[66]

- chemical changes, enzyme, immunologic, hormonal, and hematologic alterations[67]
- widespread oxidative stress and attempts by the fish to combat this damaging process[68]

It appeared that the more sophisticated the testing, such as examination with electron microscopes or analysis of the DNA, the more obvious the harm to the fish.

Amphibians such as frogs, salamanders, and snails are also vital components of healthy, biodiverse waterways. There is a 40 percent decrease in amphibians worldwide. A NLM search under the topics of amphibians and glyphosate also completed in June 2019 revealed 113 studies. Again, I examined each study published since January 2017. There were only sixteen, and of these only thirteen directly studied amphibians, glyphosate, and toxicity. These studies frequently pointed out that despite the worldwide decrease in amphibians, amphibian toxicity from environmental contamination has not been well researched. Again, however, all of the reviewed studies showed toxicity from glyphosate at different concentrations.

Tadpoles seem much more sensitive to glyphosate than fully grown frogs. One study showed that a toxin the Bufo frog produces to protect itself is made even stronger with glyphosate.[69] In the complicated way that circles of life are influenced, the Bufo's greater toxicity might then go on to harm any other species that eats them.

Summary

1. **Glyphosate-containing formulations contaminate waterways and oceans by runoff after rains.**

2. **Amounts found in these bodies of water are toxic to plankton, coral, fish, mussels, crabs, amphibians, and possibly either directly or indirectly to all life-forms in water.**

3. There is evidence that the worldwide epidemic of coral bleaching may be exacerbated or worsened by the combination of environmental pollutants and ocean warming.

4. Glyphosate may be a key contributor to the burden of environmental pollutants. New evidence of adverse effects on the microbiome of sea-going creatures creates a compelling case to further study this line of research.

8

THE BEES

Now clean cultivation and the chemical destruction of...
weeds are eliminating the last sanctuaries of these pollinating
insects and breaking the threads that bind life to life.

—*Rachael Carson, Silent Spring (1962)*

One out of every three bites of food is produced with the help of bees. This is scary information as the bee populations worldwide are in serious decline. By some estimates, bee populations have decreased by 92 percent since 1962, and over seven hundred bee species are at risk of going extinct. Unfortunately, experts continue to debate the causes of this decimation of the world's bees, even arguing if there really is a problem. Websites that support the pesticide industries point to recent data that shows the number of colonies has been holding steady in the last few years. The rebuttal by environmental groups is that the annual losses are still elevated, and the total number of colonies is only maintained by beekeepers splitting their hives and producing more colonies to match the losses. The question of whether there really is a continuing decline will become even more confusing as the USDA just announced that (despite international concerns about bee health) they will no longer compile and release annual statistics on bee populations.

Climate change, pollution, infections, and pesticides are all problems faced by bees. The pesticide blamed the most for the bee decline is in a class called neonicotinoids. These pesticides are used to coat seeds, and the evidence is strong that they play an outsized role in bee destruction.

The bee extinction started well before glyphosate became so pervasive. But once again, when you look at the studies concerning glyphosate, an alarming pattern of toxicity appears. If glyphosate is one of the villains in the bee disappearance saga, it is only one of the causative agents.

Here on Kaua'i, an impressive high school senior formed a unique partnership with an environmental group. Ritikaa Kumar was designing a science fair project and decided that she would like to check Kauai's honey for pesticides. The problem was that her equipment was primitive, and her test results might be of questionable quality, but Ritikaa had a brilliant idea.

On Kaua'i there is a wonderful organization called the Surfrider Foundation. They are a chapter of a national environmental organization started by surfers in California. It now has fifty thousand members in eighty chapters. They organize volunteers to clean beaches; they teach about the sea; they test the ocean and stream water for contaminants, and they have been a prominent voice in the problem of plastic contamination of the ocean. Kaua'i has been fortunate, one of the Surfrider leaders on the island is a retired biologist, Dr Carl Berg. He had been actively testing for pesticides and water contamination island-wide for years.

It occurred to Ritikaa that honey is a liquid. Since Surfrider tests water bodies, and they are good at what they do, she and her advisor wondered if they could convince Surfrider and Dr. Berg to work with them to improve their project's viability. Surfrider agreed to provide access to more sophisticated ELISA testing and to give advice on her sampling program. The project was award winning. This same group then went on to document the honey-glyphosate connection over three years and published their results in a peer-reviewed scientific journal. This study is now one of the significant studies in the National Library of Medicine on the subject of glyphosate and bees.[70]

They found that about 30 percent of the hives within 1 km of large-scale agriculture operations were positive for glyphosate. They also discovered an increase in positive hives closer to golf courses and roadways which are also sprayed. The levels they found are considered quite low. They are in the parts per billion range. Under current U.S. standards, these numbers are not considered dangerous to human health. But some of these samples did have levels above the European Union's acceptable levels of 50 ppb.

There are only a few studies that have looked at glyphosate in honey, and they all find that a percentage of honey samples from many different locations contain glyphosate. Ritikaa's science fair project turned science paper was the first to show that spraying activities within a kilometer of a hive significantly increase the possibility that there will be glyphosate in the honey. This is important information for two reasons:

1. Although the concentration in the honey was low, we may find that we do not want glyphosate in our food at all, particularly as it adds up.
2. Glyphosate in the honey means that glyphosate is getting into the bees and hives, and there is increasing evidence in the scientific literature that glyphosate is bad for bees.

The type of studies that I review for each of these chapters are vital to understanding any topic that has to do with science or health. Practicing physicians and scientists base their knowledge and practice decisions on studies similar to these, as well as on the opinions of experts examining these same studies.

Monsanto and the crop protection agencies keep referring to "the well-documented and researched safety record for glyphosate and products like Roundup." The clear disconnect is that the peer-reviewed published studies overwhelmingly paint a picture of glyphosate being toxic to many life-forms, and only a few studies on any of the topics I have researched for this book demonstrate that glyphosate or glyphosate-containing formulations are without toxicity even at the levels that may be found in the environment.

Returning to the studies on bees and glyphosate, in the National Library of Medicine under the topic of "bees and glyphosate," in July 2019, sixteen studies were listed that examined either toxicity or the finding of glyphosate in honey. Thirteen of them demonstrated toxicity to bees mostly at levels found in the environment, three showed no or minimal toxicity, two showed glyphosate in the honey, and one showed that bees seem to prefer glyphosate-treated plants, making the chances higher that they would ingest it and possibly transport it back to the hives.

As a general rule, the studies showing toxicities were more sophisticated research projects and used more advanced tools to examine microbiomes, cellular structure, bee learning, and genetic changes. The studies not showing toxicity were more limited in scope, examining bee or hive survival and tested for a minimal number of enzymes or other markers. Worth noting also is that only one of the studies not showing toxicity was done in the prior ten years.

The findings were that bees exposed to levels of glyphosate or Roundup found in the environment due to spraying had

- impaired colony growth and viability, and impaired ability to pollinate,[71]
- evidence of toxicity to larvae with cellular and microbiome disruption,[72,]
- microbiome disruption leading to susceptibility to lethal infections,[73]
- toxicity to a gland that bees have which secretes royal jelly, a substance used to feed the queen,[74]

- a detrimental effect on the learning needed by bees, namely the ability to smell, taste sugar, and navigate back to the hive,[75,76] and
- adverse effects on a pathway for metabolizing Vitamin A in bees.[77]

In the studies that examined glyphosate in honey, two studies showed honey to be contaminated by glyphosate,[78,79] and one study showed bees seem to prefer or were attracted to glyphosate treated plants.[80]

The following studies showed minimal to no toxicity:

- Two studies demonstrated minimal changes to a specific enzyme, vital for nerve function, that is affected by some pesticides.[81,82]
- Another study showed no changes to hive viability for hives near GMO crops vs. near non-GMO crops.[83]

The good news is that the bees on Kaua'i are considered quite healthy. That may be because the center of our island is formed by dramatic mountains and often impassable wilderness. Our agricultural footprint has been the subject of heated controversy, but it is a relatively small area; the bulk of our bees may be protected by the large part of our island not exposed to pesticides.

Summary

1. **The bee populations of the world are at risk of extinction, and bees are responsible for pollinating approximately one-third of the food we eat.**

2. **Bees active near farms, golf courses, or other places with glyphosate spraying ingest glyphosate, and low levels of this chemical may be in their honey.**

3. There are not many studies on the effect glyphosate-containing formulations have on bees, but the majority of existing studies show that glyphosate is toxic to bees at the levels found in the environment.

9

ROUNDUP AND CANCER

You can fool some of the people some of the time…
but you cannot fool all of the people all of the time.

—Attributed to various authors including
PT Barnum and Abe Lincoln

In August 2019, a judge in St. Louis rescheduled a trial which was to begin that month. The trial was rescheduled for 2020. This was the fourth trial involving a person with cancer vs. Monsanto-Bayer. In the first three cases, multimillion-dollar judgments were levied against Monsanto-Bayer. The juries found that glyphosate-containing products were the cause of the plaintiff's non-Hodgkin's lymphomas (NHL). One of the judges stated that the evidence showed "Monsanto employees crassly attempting to combat, undermine or explain away challenges to Roundup's safety."[84]

The plaintiff in this fourth case was Sharlean Gordan. She is one of seventy-five people who sued Monsanto in 2017, and her case was the first of this group to go to trial. She is in her fifties and sprayed glyphosate frequently for fifteen-plus years. She developed NHL and was treated. She was in remission in 2007 when the cancer returned. She has had two stem cell transplants and is reported to be very debilitated.

This particular case may have been more frightening to Monsanto-Bayer because in the jurisdiction of St. Louis, the trial can summon Monsanto executives as witnesses. These Monsanto executives were not permitted to be interrogated in the California cases. At the time of the printing of this book in 2020, this fourth case had not gone to trial. Instead Bayer has offered a settlement of more than ten billion dollars to greater than 100,000 claimants.

This chapter is not going to be about the evidence that Roundup may increase the risk of cancer. It is not about the extensive evidence that Monsanto engaged in activities designed to mislead the public and the world of science. Instead, this chapter is about the attempt by regulatory agencies to continue misleading the public and misleading the scientific community about the cancer-causing potential of Roundup.

I am not a conspiracy theorist. I have spent my professional life as a physician, embracing the wonders of science. The evidence does appear strong though that the United States Environmental Protection Agency (EPA) and the European Food Safety Agency (EFSA) improperly biased recent scientific reviews on the potential for glyphosate to cause cancer. It may take years to prove these reviews are scientifically flawed, but I hope that the more these stories are made public, the more transparent and objective future investigations by regulatory agencies will be.

Here is what happened. The International Agency for Research on Cancer (IARC) is a scientific committee of the United Nations. It is an international body of experts whose task is to determine if substances are likely to cause cancer. In July 2015 they announced that glyphosate was a "probable human carcinogen," meaning that there was a good possibility that it could cause cancer.[85] This sparked an almost immediate worldwide outcry of concern and has played a significant role in the tens of thousands of lawsuits now pending that allege glyphosate causes cancer. Not surprisingly there has been a vigorous pushback by Bayer-Monsanto, crop protection industries, and the food industries that still food products containing glyphosate.

The EPA and EFSA also took issue with this finding by the IARC. After their own reviews, they both stated that "glyphosate is not likely to cause cancer in humans." The pronouncements by these regulatory agencies are now a significant part of the *defense* mounted by Bayer-Monsanto against the cancer allegations.

Numerous authors have published detailed and dueling reviews, including a consensus statement by ninety-four scientists deeply criticizing the methods for evaluation used by these two regulatory agencies.[86] Below, I explore the EPA's methods, but those used by the EFSA were quite similar.

In 2016, the EPA published an eagerly awaited scientific review that, as mentioned, "found that glyphosate is not likely to cause cancer." It turns out that their investigation was different in its conclusions from the IARC for a number of reasons. These reasons were well outlined in an article written by Dr. Charles Benbrook and I have summarized the points he made in the material below[87]:

1. Dr. Benbrook describes how the EPA gave the most weight to studies examining glyphosate in its technical form; that is almost pure glyphosate. The problem with that is glyphosate is never used in its pure form by homeowners, farmers, or gardeners. It is only used in formulations containing many other chemicals (GBHs). These other chemicals are mostly designed to help move glyphosate into the cells of plants to better kill them. These same mechanisms work on the cells of mammals. Numerous studies have shown that glyphosate in formulation is much more toxic than technical or pure glyphosate. As a result of this difference in focus, IARC reported on 118 studies which looked at both technical grade and glyphosate formulations. The EPA only evaluated 51 of those studies, and then because 24 of these 51 studies evaluated the glyphosate formulation, the

BREAKFAST AT MONSANTO'S

EPA ended up only giving weight to 27 of the original 118 evaluations. In addition, because herbicide sprayers never use technical glyphosate, there are no studies showing the effect of technical grade or pure glyphosate on humans. Because EPA gave more weight to the reviews on technical glyphosate, *they were able to say that there is very little evidence of harm to humans—basically because there are no studies of technical glyphosate on humans!* The EPA's opposition to giving weight to studies with glyphosate formulations resulted in three human studies showing linkage to cancer not getting the attention by the EPA that was given to them by the IARC.

2. The EPA also gave the most weight to registrant commissioned studies. These are studies paid for by the company which produces the product. These studies frequently are unpublished, not peer-reviewed, and are often not available to the general public. The EPA gave much less weight or importance to the studies done by scientists around the world that are peer reviewed, published, and available for all to examine. Consider this: 99 percent of the registrant-commissioned studies showed no harm, while 70 percent of the published, peer-reviewed studies showed toxicity. Not only did the EPA only look at 27 of the studies mentioned above, but when they evaluated the evidence that glyphosate *is* toxic to genes (DNA), they looked in addition at another 109 assays performed by the registrants, and again, as in other studies paid for by the companies, only 6.4 percent of these studies showed harm.

3. If the first two reasons were not astounding enough, the EPA also looked at very different exposure data. The EPA looked at the type of glyphosate exposure one has from general public dietary exposure. By comparison, the IARC also examined studies that evaluated the cancer risk of those people who'd had more significant contact—such as those who spray glyphosate formulations. People who regularly

spray and work with glyphosate have a much higher risk than the general public. The lawsuits to date have been by plaintiffs who heavily used or were heavily exposed to glyphosate. We may prove someday that glyphosate in our food may also cause cancer, but special consideration should have been given to the risk of cancer in those with heavier exposures.

The data reviewed by IARC is strengthened by other studies they referenced. They included an additional 82 assays demonstrating other mechanisms for gene toxicity, such as sex hormone disruption and evidence of oxidative stress. This refers to the process in which the normal functioning of a cell is harmed by the production of too many waste products, known as free radicals. Oxidative stress is a major driver of inflammation and ill-health. Glyphosate formulations have been shown to induce oxidative stress.

As mentioned in Chapter 4, the finding that glyphosate probably causes cancer has been given increased credibility by a study published by the University of Washington in 2019. They found a 41 percent increase in the risk of NHL in those who had heavy exposures.

Summary

1. **In 2015, the International Agency for Research on Cancer (IARC) published its finding that "glyphosate probably causes cancer."**

2. **Major regulatory bodies such as the European Food Safety Association (EFSA) and the United States Environmental Protection Agency (EPA) performed their own reviews and stated that it is "unlikely" that glyphosate causes cancer.**

3. Around the world, scientists and regulatory bodies are debating these differing opinions. Expert opinions including consensus statements by scientists have stated that the findings of the EPA and the EFSA are deeply flawed for the following reasons:

   A. They relied mostly on industry-produced research that was usually not published, or peer reviewed, or even available for review by the public.

   B. They gave much higher weight to studies examining the technical grade glyphosate, which is quite different than the formulations used in the real world. Glyphosate formulations such as Roundup contain numerous chemicals designed to make glyphosate more potent as an herbicide and are more toxic to other organisms.

   C. The exposure data they reviewed was mostly the exposure that results from glyphosate in our food supply. They did not specifically review the much higher exposures of those who work with or are around spraying operations. Pending lawsuits alleging glyphosate-caused cancer are from plaintiffs with this type of greater exposure.

10

DEPRESSION

When you suffer from depression, 'I'm tired' means
a permanent state of exhaustion that sleep doesn't fix.

—Healthyplace.com

The statistics about depression are sobering and deserve a lot of attention:

1. According to the World Health Organization, the rate of depression in the United States is the second highest in the world, exceeded only by the Ukraine. In 2017, WHO reported that 5.9 percent of the US population meets the criteria for depression.[88]
2. Some sources show that the incidence of depression in the United States has increased 10 percent since 2005.[89]
3. Suicide is also on the rise. Life expectancy in the United States has decreased for the first time in modern history, and part of that decrease is attributable to higher suicide rates.
4. The age adjusted rate of suicide has increased 30 percent between 2000 and 2016.[90]

5. Suicide among farmers has also received more publicity. Some studies have shown that farmers are committing suicide at one and a half to two times the rate of the general public.

According to an article in *The Guardian*[91]:

> The U.S. farmer suicide crisis echoes a much larger farmer suicide crisis happening globally: an Australian farmer dies by suicide every four days; in the UK, one farmer a week takes his or her own life; in France, one farmer dies by suicide every two days; in India, more than 270,000 farmers have died by suicide since 1995.

A recent Canadian study of 1,132 farmers found that 34 percent were possibly depressed and 15 percent were probably depressed.[92] News articles about rising suicide rates tend to differ around the world. In India, the media frequently states that pesticides play a role. In the United States, blame is more often attributed to a difficult lifestyle, a culture of stoicism, and economic pressures.

The Guardian article described in great detail the hard work, isolation, financial risk, and physical risk farmers deal with daily. All of those factors so poignantly described in that article are certainly true, but pesticide use may well be another factor.

Peer-reviewed published research papers show a direct correlation between a certain type of pesticide and depression. A pesticide in the organophosphate (OP) class kills insects by altering the chemical balance in their nerve pathways. It is known to have a similar effect on human nerve pathways, so precautions are recommended in the use of this type of chemical. These chemicals, such as chlorpyrifos, are in the class of restricted use pesticides as their toxicity is well established. Studies have shown, however, that even at levels of exposure that lab testing deems low, this chemical does affect farmworkers, and it is directly correlated with depression.[93] Additional studies have shown increases in depression in adolescents growing up in or near farming communities.[94] In Tanzania[95] flower growers with pesticide exposure had increased depression, and in Korea[96] pesticide applicators had rates of depression that correlated with higher use of pesticides. These studies leave little doubt that some of the pesticides farmers are using can and do cause depression.

Research also suggests that glyphosate formulations are adding to the rising rate of depression. Two recent studies looked at rats with chronic exposure to doses of glyphosate. These doses were either at the full concentration or half the concentration known to cause harmful effects. After chronic exposure, the rats in both studies had increased anxiety and increased depression. (Yes, scientists can measure anxiety and depression in rats.) Researchers discovered that some of the changes in the rats' brain chemicals were similar to changes caused by the OP insecticides.[97] This is alarming because as mentioned above the OP pesticides are known neurotoxins. The researchers also demonstrated significant changes in the gastro-intestinal microflora of these rats after exposure.[98]

Research completed in August 2019 revealed 40 studies published in the National Library of Medicine under the topic of the microbiome and glyphosate. Most showed that glyphosate alters the microbiome. There were 662 studies published on the topic of depression and the microbiome. A large number of these showed a connection exists between alterations in intestinal bacteria and depression. It is only circumstantial evidence to formally conclude that since glyphosate affects the microbiome of animals and since changes in the microbiome causes depression, the amount of glyphosate that we receive in our food or the amount farmers are exposed to definitely causes depression. But there is a strong possibility that they are related. The amount of glyphosate the planet is now exposed to is huge, and the possible connection merits further study.

The few studies we have directly linking glyphosate to depression are worrisome. And as depression and suicide are so prevalent in the farming world, much more importance should be given to the very clear evidence that OP pesticides do cause depression. There are readily available blood tests for acytylcholinesterase, which is the enzyme affected by OP pesticides. I believe the evidence is strong enough that any farmer or person living in a farm community who presents with depression should be tested for this enzyme.

On Kaua'i, as part of our work on the pesticide task force, we visited the seed farms. They had multimillion-dollar spraying units with airconditioned cabs and nozzles that delivered pinpoint sprays to their crops. The farm managers also told us that they regularly checked the applicator's blood levels for the enzyme mentioned above. Looking at this high-tech cab, it seemed obvious that the exposure of these drivers in these sealed cabs was probably much less than the people working in the fields. We asked if they also checked the blood levels of those that worked in the fields. Their answer was no.

One of the issues affecting the idea that pesticides might be a causative factor of depression in farmers has to do with a cultural phenomenon even apparent on Kaua'i. People who worry about pesticides tend to be viewed as tree-hugging hippies or crazy extreme environmentalists. Farm culture is rugged, and the average farmer may not want to be viewed as a radical environmentalist. Also, the journals they read are very much influenced by the crop-protection industries.

This may be changing. There are over 100,000 plaintiffs in the Roundup lawsuits. That's a lot of people who believe this pesticide harmed them. But, if Bayer puts billions of dollars on the table to settle the lawsuits, will we all go back to forgetting that Roundup is not as safe as Bayer-Monsanto claims it to be and continue ignoring the role that pesticides may play in neurobehavioral impairments?

■ ■ ■

I have saved this next section for last because the research is so pre-liminary, but it may well turn out to contain the most important clue of all to the relationship between glyphosate and depression.

There have been hundreds of articles written in the past five years about the possible role that glutamate (a chemical found in the brain) may have in producing or worsening depression. Inflammation, genetics, certain chemicals, and other factors appear to excite the glutamate pathway. When this pathway is excited, depression may get worse, and when this pathway is mod-ulated or brought under more control, depression may decrease.

Two drugs that have been used for years as anesthetics, ket-amine and nitrous oxide or laughing gas, are both attracting great interest because they lessen depression. The effects of these drugs are so dramatic that a person may feel less depressed in minutes after treatments, and even better, the effect may last for some time. My dentist uses laughing gas, and I know first-hand how enjoyable even dental procedures are while you are breathing the gas. The evidence keeps growing that these drugs work by calming down or decreasing the effect of glutamate. The dramatic effect of nitrous oxide and ketamine in decreasing depression appears to provide further evidence that the glutamate pathway is a vital component in the mechanism of mood disorders.

This brings us back to glyphosate. Rats treated with chronic exposure to Roundup clearly had evidence of the glutamate path-way becoming overactive or excited.[99] These rats with their over-active glutamate pathways also exhibited measurable markers of depression.

This whole area needs much more research, but the clues are very suggestive that chronic exposure to GBHs does affect gluta-mate in a way that is associated with depression. We may be the second-most depressed nation in the world for the same reason we are among the most obese of nations. Roundup in our food may well be making us fatter, sicker, and sadder.

Summary

1. The United States has the second-highest incidence of depression in world. Rates of suicide and depression are also increasing around the world.

2. Suicide in farmers is at a greater rate than in the general public, and there is a high rate in farmers around the world.

3. A common class of pesticide, organophosphates (OPs), has been linked to depression in those exposed and should more commonly be considered and tested for in members of farming communities.

4. Recent studies in rats showed exposure to glyphosate increased depression and anxiety. It is worrisome that the mechanisms underlying the increase in depression may include alterations to the rat microbiome and biochemical changes in the brain. These brain changes were similar to those alterations found with OP pesticides.

5. The biochemical changes affected by GBHs also include excitation of the glutamate pathway. Excitation of this pathway is increasingly accepted as a biochemical component of depression.

11

DIRT AND TREES

The nation that destroys its soil, destroys itself.

—Franklin Delano Roosevelt

The movie *Avatar* was one of the highest-grossing movies ever. In the movie, a network of trees had more interconnections than the human brain and contributed to the intelligence and knowledge of the planet's inhabitants. A mother tree served as a protector and wisdom keeper for the planet.

A best seller in twelve countries, *The Hidden Life of Trees, What They feel, How they Communicate* was written by a German forester, Peter Wohlleben. The author spent the first part of his life as a traditional forest worker using bulldozers and pesticides. He spent the later part of his life studying and writing about the magical qualities of trees. He convinced his village to *not* cut their forest for profit but instead to care for it by promoting the relationship between the trees. The beauty and mystical qualities of this forest made it a major tourist attraction.

The shared theme in these two success stories is a description of tree magic. Scientists from around the world have come to realize that forests are wonders of interconnections. One of the key links is through microscopic tendrils of fungi. One teaspoon of soil has miles of these filaments. These threads of life act not only as the nervous system of the forest but also as capillaries of nutrition. This network binds the forest into a woven basket of life. Mother trees feed their saplings as the saplings do not have sufficient sunlight to make their own sugars. If sections of the forest need help, nutrients are sent through these fungal capillaries from the stronger trees. For example, bears eat salmon under trees by the river, and the nitrogen from those salmon carcasses is found in trees far from the river. And trees don't just work to help their own kind; this network appears to work at keeping the whole forest healthy. The web of life between trees is gaining increasing attention and imaginative folklore. Forests can be better understood as living organisms in their own right. Like our human body with its networks of bacteria, blood vessels, chemicals, and nerves, forests and fields are also networks. When examined in aggregate, they act as a living, breathing, perhaps at some basic level, even conscious systems of life.

My wife and I traveled extensively in Myanmar. One of the trips was up to the Chinese border. Agriculture near the border is a clash of extremes. Around each small village is a vegetable and fruit garden. These gardens look wild and are full of food. A short distance away are fields that appear perfect: straight rows of crops with no weeds at all. These perfect-looking fields are enormous. We were told that each wild-appearing vegetable-and-fruit-filled garden is the village's food basket. The big perfect-appearing fields are run by the Chinese. They are farming intensively on Myanmar lands and most likely are heavily using pesticides. Sections of this border with China were partially off limits because rebels have been fighting for years to have more control of their own lands. Unfortunately, the people that control Myanmar appear to prefer money from China to local indigenous ownership.

When a chemical is used to free a field of weeds, it means the soil and land between these rows of crops are dramatically altered. Studies show that soil bacteria and fungi are altered by Roundup exposure: some bacterial and fungal strains become stronger, and some become weaker.[100] In addition, Roundup affects soil nutrients as it binds with certain metals, and it also may release phosphate, as phosphate is in the pesticide. It is becoming clear that just as Roundup is upsetting the balance of bacteria in and on our bodies, it is affecting the interconnected vibrancy of a field or forest. Making these changes even worse is that they persist. Monsanto claims that glyphosate rapidly degrades in soil, and even that appears to often not be true. In Finland, Roundup has persisted in fields all winter, and studies have shown its persistence in the soil for up to four hundred days.[101]

The research is quite convincing that Roundup does affect the teeming life of healthy soil. An important question is whether these effects on the environment have an effect on human and animal health. A recent literature review done by researchers at the University of Florida concludes that there is evidence that the bacterial alterations in soil and plants may make plant infections harder to control. Further, bacterial changes in soil could play a role in altering human bacterial ratios. They may even have the very dangerous effect of promoting antibiotic resistance.[102] They conclude that this is a very important topic and needs much more research.

We should be concerned that glyphosate is altering the webs of life in these fields, and this alteration is not good for the planet or its inhabitants. More research is needed, but the research we have already should affect regulatory decisions.

One reason to make regulatory changes sooner rather than later has to do with how regulatory bodies determine what are safe levels for any pesticide in food products. Maximum Regulatory Levels (MRLs) are the greatest amount of any chemical that is allowed in various foods. These amounts differ widely in different foods and are essentially higher in the United States. The higher levels permissible in the United States may be a direct result of the outsized influence corporations have on regulations in the United States.

According to the pesticide industry, these levels are set by the amount that you might find in food if the pesticide was applied to plants according to the label—that is, if the pesticide was sprayed properly. But there is no easy equation to figure out if the amount in the food is safe. The contents of this book and the hundreds of studies offer clear evidence that there is no agreement on what level is safe in food. So, when corporations assure us that glyphosate in our Cheerios does not reach a level of concern, they mean that glyphosate levels are not at the maximum regulatory level. Also to be noted is that these distressing MRLs are increasing as it takes more Roundup to kill newly emerging resistant weeds.

Summary

1. The soil in a forest or a field is similar to the microbiome of all life-forms. When it is healthy, it is teeming with life. The life in soil includes bacteria, fungi, bugs, and worms. In a healthy forest, a teaspoon of soil holds miles of fungal filaments. These fungal filaments act as complex connectors, providing information and nourishment. Pesticides as a class and glyphosate formulations in particular alter these webs of life, changing the balance and decreasing the biologic diversity.

2. Research institutions are demonstrating that we should be concerned that altering the soil may decrease our food's nutritional quality and increase their health risk.

12

THE WIZARD AND THE PROPHET

- *In fact, humans have caused the annihilation of 83% of all wild mammals and half of all plants...Of the birds left in the world, 70% are poultry chickens and other farmed birds. And of the mammals left in the world, 60% are livestock, 36% are pigs, and a mere 4% are wild.*

—Environment, 2018

- *Severe poverty has decreased from 35% of the world's population in 1987 to 11% in 2013.*
- *Level of hunger in the world has decreased by 27% since 2000.*
- *Child labor decreased by 40% between 2000 and 2016.*
- *Food cost in America has decreased from 17.5% of a person's income to 9.6% since 1960.*
- *World child mortality has fallen by more than one half since 1990.*
- *Illiteracy rates have fallen dramatically around the world.*

—VOX, 2018

The statements above represent two truths about the current world. Corporate interests and technology are raising the world out of starvation and poverty and at the same time degrading the planet. Somehow, we need to learn how to respond to both with wisdom and a plan of action.

This book is mainly about the emerging evidence that herbicide formulations containing glyphosate are much more toxic in our food and our environment than has been appreciated. But pesticides are part of a much more complicated issue concerning the wonders of technology versus the potential horrors of technology advancing without planetary stewardship.

In Charles Mann's wonderful book, *The Wizard and The Prophet*,[103] he wrote of two men, neither particularly well known, who had major impacts on agriculture in the world today. The two men, Norman Borlaug and William Vogt, had starkly different views. They met only once, and the meeting did not go well.

Both were born in the early 1900s. Vogt became one of the founding members of the current environmental movement. He represented the prophet. He stated that "less is more," and that we will be destroyed by rampant consumerism.[90(p6)] Vogt worried about technology developing unchecked, and he played a significant role in warning the world against growth without consideration of consequences.

Norman Borlaug was the wizard. The wizards believe that technology is the answer to the world's ills. Borlaug put his beliefs into action. He is often thought of as the father of the green revolution (not the Green New Deal).[90(p6)] His thinking, creativity, and drive played a significant role in dramatically increasing grain production per acre worldwide. Some credit him with playing a significant role in saving the lives of a billion people. Borlaug's methods consisted of highly scientific plant breeding, synthetic fertilizers, and modern farming tools.

The author, Charles Mann, states that the battle between prophets and wizards has gotten worse since the time of these two men. He describes the growing intensity of the fight as "dialogues of the deaf."[90(p7)] He says this might be all right "if we weren't discussing the fate of our children." An obvious answer lies in a road between the two camps, but Mann states it is difficult to create this dialogue or walk the middle path.

This debate between the prophet and the wizard began well before crops were genetically engineered or Roundup became so pervasive. The difficulty in finding a middle way is evident in the battle over genetically modified foods and the heavy use of herbicides. Roundup-ready crops are now deeply embedded in the current American agricultural system. They decrease the labor needed to produce crops, and they allow farmers to avoid tilling the land to kill weeds. As a general rule, not tilling is good for the soil and is good for the climate as not tilling improves carbon sequestration. Roundup is actually just one more tool used in the science of monoculture agriculture, and even if Roundup went away, the original conflict between high-yield profitable farming and concern for the environment would still need to be addressed. The debate is driven by profit motives, the wonders of technology, the need to feed 7.5 billion people, and the clear need for better planetary stewardship.

Monoculture cropping describes the growing of one crop at a time on a given field. It also applies to animals in the factory farms, as these industries grow cows, chickens, and pigs under intense conditions. There are definite pros and cons to monoculture systems.[104] The points below were summarized from an article by Sara Slavikova (Greentumble, 2019).

1. Specialization allows economies of scale. It is easier to plan for single crops.
2. In large monoculture systems, farmers are more likely to buy highly specialized machines, and often this increases efficiency.
3. Due to increased efficiency, there is the ability to increase profits and decrease labor costs. Management may also be easier with less crop diversification.
4. Yield per acre also tends to increase when all the focus is on fewer crops.
5. Other authors have noted that higher yield per acre may allow more land to stay forested as it is not needed for crops.

The disadvantages of monoculture are also significant:

1. Pest problems often worsen, and the use of pesticides increases as loss of biodiversity tends to promote pest abundance. Pests appear to thrive on adapting to single crops.
2. An increase in pests and the increase in pesticides leads to the increase in pesticide resistance, which leads to more pesticides.
3. Even with crop rotation, intensive farming often degrades the soil. The UN estimates that one-third of the planet's soils are degraded due to farming methods.
4. Because soils tend to deteriorate with monoculture, there is a need for more fertilizers.
5. More fertilizers and more pesticides result in more runoff of chemicals. These runoffs are blamed for toxic algae blooms, death of aquatic species, pollution of lakes and rivers, and huge dead zones like the 8,000 square miles in the Gulf of Mexico which is empty of marine life. The EPA was quoted in this article as saying that agriculture pollutes at least 48 percent of rivers and 41 percent of lakes in America.
6. Nitrogen-containing fertilizers and cattle factory farms lead to the emissions of nitrous oxide and methane. Both these greenhouse gases are contributing to climate change.
7. Monocropping may lead to compacted, depleted soils and require more irrigation.
8. The increase in the yields of soy, corn, oats, and wheat feed the ultra-processed food industry. The resulting tasty, addictive factory foods lead to a significant decrease in diversity in the average American's diet, worsening the health of the consumers.

■ ■ ■

I also agree that the answer lies between the two camps. Advances in technology and stewardship for the planet need to join forces. One impediment to the needed cooperation is the profit motive built into large corporations. Executives in any corporation are rewarded for meeting or exceeding financial goals. Administrators are selected in terms of traits that can help achieve these business goals. Good people try to do a good job for their company, and the planet suffers. Somehow planet and human stewardship goals need to be woven into the fabric of evaluating corporations, evaluating their leaders and most certainly in evaluating governments. Total environmental costs must be part of the equation. We have cheap food, but the consumption of this cheap food is a significant driver of sky-high healthcare costs. Those healthcare costs may bankrupt the nation, and they have certainly bankrupted many individuals.

Summary

1. The degradation of nature is accelerating, *and* the people of the world are being lifted out of poverty and starvation.

2. Our food industry is locked in a titanic struggle created by the interface of the need to feed 7.5 billion people, emerging technologies used to enhance food production, the profit motive of agribusiness, and the rapidly increasing degradation of planet earth.

3. Monoculture agriculture, genetic engineering, and the heavy use of fertilizers and pesticides have helped feed the world, but they are also part of the problem.

4. The prophets and wizards of the world need to join forces.

13

WHERE DO WE GO FROM HERE?

Two roads diverged in a yellow woods.

—*Robert Frost*

I hope by the time you reach this chapter, I have opened your mind to the possibility that glyphosate-containing products may be harmful to humans and to most other life-forms. Scientists from around the world have published large amounts of evidence demonstrating that formulations containing glyphosate are toxic to microbiomes, genetic material, cellular structures, enzymes systems, neurotransmitters, and many other building blocks of life.

Chemical companies often state that a cardinal rule of science is that the "dose makes the poison."[105] Monsanto claims that glyphosate is one of the safest pesticides on the market, but science is demonstrating that the 9.4 million tons sprayed on fields around the world may create a dose meeting the definition of a poison. Science is also discovering that substances can be harmful even at very low doses. Emerging research shows that low doses of glyphosate can affect hormones and can alter the bacteria that coexist with us and are vital for all life-forms.

...

I believe for all the problems facing the world an individual can ask, what can I change in my own life that might make the problem better and what can I do as a member of society? I divided my thoughts on possible actions into these two categories.

Suggested actions for an individual

1. Decrease the amount of glyphosate you are taking in with your food.
2. This means decrease consumption of Roundup-ready, GMO crops. Try not to eat nonorganic foods that contain soy, corn, or canola. In America, they are almost all Roundupready. This isn't easy! One or more of those three named ingredients are in most ultra-processed food in America.
3. When possible, eat organic grains. Avoid nonorganic bread and nonorganic breakfast cereals. GBHs are often sprayed on non-GMO crops like wheat, oats, and rice before harvest. Understand that a product may be GMO free and still may be coated with GBHs.
4. Avoid most nonorganic sweeteners as they often are from GMO sugar beets, high fructose corn syrup (made from GMO corn), or sugar cane that has been sprayed with GBHs to increase the sugar content.
5. I think it is important to add that not all genetically engineered or GMO foods may need to be avoided. Here in Hawai`i, the papaya industry was in trouble because of a virus killing the papaya. Scientists were able to genetically engineer the papaya to resist this viral infection and saved the crop. In this case the engineering did not lead to using more pesticides and I know of no reason to avoid this food.

General tips on eating

The evidence is clear that ultra-processed foods are a major cause of worldwide poor health. GBHs in our food are just part of that problem. In a concise and engaging fashion, Michael Pollan outlines eating guidelines in his wonderful book, *Food Rules.*[106] I add to his rules by saying, "Eat organic whenever possible." Stores are adding many more organic products, and it is easier than ever before to follow this advice.

Food Rules, according to Michael Pollan:

- "Eat food, not too much, mostly green."[92(p17)]

By food, he means "real food," not food made in a factory that no longer even looks like food. He uses the following powerful phases to describe what he means by real foods:

- "Don't Eat Anything Your Great Grandmother Wouldn't Recognize as Food."[92(p46)]
- "If It Came from a Plant, Eat It; If It Was Made in a Plant, Don't."[92(p79)]

He does not say one has to avoid meats altogether but does make the point that plant-based diets are healthier. He quotes a Chinese saying[92(p99)]:

> "Eating what stands on one leg (mushrooms and plants) is better than eating what stands on two legs (fowl), which is better than eating what stands on four legs (cows, pigs, and other mammals)."

Pollan also warns about sweeteners and suggests not eating any high fructose syrup and not eating any food where sugar is in the top three ingredients.[92(pp52-53)]

Big industries now have a major role in producing organic products, and we may increasingly find corporate shortcuts making even this food less healthy. If you drive around California, you will see large fields covered with plastic. They are growing certified organic crops. Plastic-impregnated soils may not be good for us or for the earth. Hopefully, products like hemp will take plastic out of our lives, but we all need to stay vigilant about all aspects of our food production.

Suggested actions as a member of society

1. Vote with your dollar. Avoid purchasing ultra-processed foods, Roundup-ready/GMO foods, or grains sprayed with GBHs. If you can afford it, buy mostly organic. The more we vote with our dollar, the more we send a message to the producers.

2. Lobby for the use of the precautionary principle in the approval of chemicals that we may be exposed to. The precautionary principle is part of the European Union's regulatory process. It is actually a very complex concept which roughly calls for erring on the side of safety. The general principle is that a process or product should be *shown to be safe* before it is used, or before its approval is renewed.[107] In the United States, our guideline often appears to be that a substance needs to be *demonstrated to be harmful* before it is removed or denied access to markets. It's even sometimes stated that a chemical should *not* be removed if the economic impact of discontinuation is too great. An example of the difference in this approach to safety is that the amount of glyphosate humans may be exposed to is more than three times higher in the U.S. than the E.U.[108]

3. Strengthen the defenses against financial interests distorting science. The tobacco industries; the food processing companies; the sugar, dairy, and meat industries; and the chemical-seed companies have all played a role in misleading us. They have also convinced regulatory agencies to distort truths. In well-documented instances, financial

interests have persuaded scientists from reputable institutions to write or sign review articles that fly in the face of the preponderance of evidence.

I believe one of the reasons that the anti-vaccination movement has gained so much strength is that the profit motive has distorted science, and we all know it. When young parents see this perversion of science for profit in all these other industries, they are worried that the vaccination industry is just one more example of this, and it has become much harder for pediatricians like me to convince them otherwise. Here is the text from one of the jury findings in a recent Bayer-Monsanto court case[109]:

> "The jury also found that Monsanto acted with malice, oppression or fraud and should be punished for its conduct."

How then can members of society make sure corporate interests don't distort science? I believe we can do the following:

1. Elect leaders who will work to better regulate the role of money in politics. Citizens United should be overturned. Large corporations are not people, and they should not be able to buy elections or officials.
2. Make it a law and a standard that nobody with a conflict of interest can be a top administrator in a regulatory agency. The EPA has become a revolving door for past employees of chemical companies. This is a serious conflict of interest as the role of the EPA is to regulate chemicals in our environment. That same type of improperly cozy relationship with industry is visible in other agencies set up to protect us, such as the Department of Energy and the Department of Agriculture.

3. This same standard needs to be enforced for any agency or commission tasked with making recommendations that affect populations. If you have a conflict of interest, you should not sit on a body making policy recommendations.
4. Food products need to be tested for pesticide residues and labeled with the pesticides they contain.
5. As discussed in Chapter 12, the challenge is to get wizards and prophets to work together. We have huge global challenges. Science and modern technology are a vital part of the solution, but proposed solutions need to be analyzed constantly and transparently for potential harms.

The window may be closing on maintaining a planet suitable for human habitation. We must adopt the precautionary principle. We must create a government and corporate ethic that evaluates all scientific advances against possible harms and makes walking the middle road the right path for us all.

CLOSING STATEMENT

Just weeks before the publication of this book, environmental organizations sued the EPA for not properly evaluating the growing scientific documentation of the toxicity of glyphosate based products. The lawsuit reviews the evidence of this toxicity including the U.S. regulatory agencies recent determination that glyphosate "is likely to adversely affect 1,676 species of birds, mammals, fish, plants, amphibians, insects, and more."

I hope my short book helps bring these same concerns to the general public. The chemical-seed companies and the crop protection industries continue to say that glyphosate-based herbicides (GBHs) are safe. Yet, the scientific evidence is strong that these substances are potentially toxic in the quantities and formulations that populations are being exposed to. I agree with the environmental groups that the evidence is strong enough that regulatory agencies need to take a fresh look at these formulations.

Science and the regulatory agencies should be asking and answering the following questions:

- Has all of the new information concerning the potential toxicity of GBHs been properly assessed and is this information properly driving the regulation of these pesticides?

- Are we properly studying the possible additional toxic effects of glyphosate being used in formulations with other chemicals?
- What new studies need to be done to demonstrate that the amount of glyphosate the world is being exposed to is safe or unsafe?
- What actions should the regulatory agencies be taking *now* to ensure that our food and environment is not being adversely affected by the tons of GBHs currently used worldwide?

I include below a short bibliography to supplement the large number of citations in the reference section of this book. The material below is valuable to read as each of these documents gives an overview of the many concerns described in the scientific literature and discussed in this book. The final reference cited is a book by Carey Gillam. Her book describes in great detail the very disturbing tactics used by Monsanto to maintain the image of Roundup's safety. Her book won the 2018 Rachael Carson book award.

Suggested Additional Reading

1. Link to 12/2020 lawsuit against the EPA for failure to properly evaluate glyphosate based products. https://www.centerforfoodsafety.org/files/01-rc-opening-brief-corrected_27232.pdf
2. Peillex C, Pelletier M. The impact and toxicity of glyphosate and glyphosate-based herbicides on health and immunity. *J Immunotoxicol.* 2020;17(1):163-174
3. Vandenberg LN, Blumberg B, Antoniou MN, et al. Is it time to reassess current safety standards for glyphosate-based herbicides? *J Epidemiol Community Health.* 2017 Jun;71(6):613-618

4. Myers JP, Antoniou MN, Blumberg B, et al. Concerns over use of glyphosate-based herbicides and risks associated with exposures: a consensus statement. *Environ Health*. 2016 Feb 17;15:19

5. Gillam C. *Whitewash: The Story of a Weedkiller, Cancer, and the Corruption of Science*. Washington, DC: Island Press; 2017

REFERENCES

1   Roberts J, Karr C. American Academy of Pediatrics, Council on Environmental health. Technical Report—pesticide exposure in children. *Pediatrics.* 2012;130(6):e1765-e1788

2   Roberts J, Karr C. American Academy of Pediatrics, Council on Environmental health. Policy Statement—pesticide exposure in children. *Pediatrics.* 2012;130(6):e1757-e1763

3   Pesticide Use by Large Agribusinesses on Kaua'i. *Accord3.0 Website.* http://www.accord3.com/pg1000.cfm

4   Committee Opinion. Exposure to toxic environmental agents. *Obstet-Gynecol in Conjunction with USC.* 2013;122(4):931-935(Reaffirmed 2018)

5   Di Renzo GC, Conry JA, Blake J, et al. International Federation of Gynecology and Obstetrics Opinion on Reproductive Health Impacts of Exposure to Toxic Environmental Chemicals. *Int J Gynecol Obstet.* 2015;131(3):219-225

6   Swanson N, Leu A, Abrahamson J, et al. Genetically engineered crops, glyphosate and the deterioration of health in the United States of America. *J Org Syst.* 2014;9(2)

7   Eskenazi B, Huen K, Marks A, et al. PON1 and neurodevelopment in children from the CHAMACOS study exposed to organophosphate pesticides in utero. *Environ Health Perspec.* 2010;118(12):1775–1781

8   Rauh VA, Perara FP, Horton MK, et al. Brain anomalies and pesticide exposure. *Proc Natl Acad Sci.* 2012;109(20):7871-7876

9   Pesticide Use by Large Agribusinesses on Kaua'i. *Accord3.0 Website*, Appendix 2: 264, http://www.accord3.com/pg1000.cfm

10   Vandenberg LN, Blumberg B, Antoniou MN, et al. Is it time to reassess current safety standards for glyphosate-based herbicides?.*J Epidemiol Community Health.* 2017;71(6):613-618

11   Antoniou M, Habib MEM, Howard CV, et al. Teratogenic effects of glyphosate-based herbicides: divergence of regulatory decisions from scientific evidence. *J Environ Anal Toxicol.* 2012;S4:006

12   Mesnage R, Defarge N, Rocque L-M, Spiroux de Vendomois J, Serilini G-E. Laboratory rodent diets contain toxic levels of environmental contaminants: implications for regulatory tests. *PLoS One.* 2015;10(7):e0128429

13   CDC. Antibiotic Resistance Threats in the United States, 2019. Atlanta, GA: *U.S. Department of Health and Human Services, CDC*; 2019

14   Vuong HE, Hsiao EY. Emerging roles for the gut microbiome in autism spectrum disorder. *Biol Psychiatry.* 2017;81(5):411–423

15   Sampson TR, Debelius JW, Thron T, et al. Gut microbiota regulate motor deficits and neuroinflammation in a model of Parkinson's disease. *Cell.* 2016;1167(6):1469–1480

16   Jiag C, Li G, Huang P, Liu Z, Zhao B. The gut microbiota and Alzheimers's disease. *J Alzheimers Dis.* 2017;58(1):1–15

17   Kang DW, Adams JB, Coleman, DM, et al. Long-term benefits of microbiota transfer therapy on autism symptoms and gut microbiota. *Sci Rep.* 2019;9(1):5821

18   Lozano VL, Defarge N, N, Rocque LM, et al. Sex-dependent impact of Roundup on rat microbiome. *Toxicol Rep.* 2018;5:96–107

19   Aitbali Y, Ba-M'hamed S, Elihidar N, Nafis A, Soraa N, Bennis M. Glyphosate-based herbicide exposure affects gut microbiota,

anxiety and depression-like behaviors in mice. *Neurotoxicol Teratol.* 2018;67:44–49

20 Vanjay P, Johnson AJ, Ward TL, et al. US immigration western-izes the human gut microbiome. *Cell.* 2018;175(4):962–972

21 Kurenbach B, Marjoshi D, Carlos F, et al. Sublethal exposure to commercial formulations of the herbicides dicamba, 2,4-dichlorophenoxyacetic acid, and glyphosate cause changes in antibiotic susceptibility in escherichia coli and salmonella enterica serovar typhimurium. *mBio6.* 2015; 6(2):e00009-15

22 Kurenbach B, Gibson PS, Hill AM, et al. Herbicide ingredients change salmonella enterica vs. typhimurium and escherichia coli antibiotic responses. *Microbiology.* 2017; 163: 1791-1801

23 Kurenbach B, Hill AM, Godsoe W, van Hamelsveld S, Heinnemann JA. Agrichemicals and antibiotics in combination increase antibiotic resistance evolution. *PeerJ.* 2018;(6):5801

24 Eick V, Motta S, Raymann K, Moran NA. Glyphosate perturbs the gut microbiota of honey bees. *PNAS.* 2018;115(41):10305–10310

25 Dai P, Yan Z, Ma S, et al. The herbicide glyphosate nega-tively affects midgut bacterial communities and survival of honey bee during larvae reared in vitro. *J Agric Food Chem.* 2018;66(29):7786–7793

26 Shehata AA, Schrodll W, Aldin AA, Hafez HM, Kroger M. The effect of glyphosate on potential pathogens and beneficial mem-bers of poultry microbiota in vitro. *Curr Microbiol.* 2013;4:350

27 Schrodl W, Kruger S, Konstantinova-Muller T, Shehata AA, Rulff R. Kruger M. Possible effects of glyphosate on mucora-les abundance in the rumen of dairy cows in Germany. *Curr Microbiol.* 2014;69(6):817–823

28 Kremer RJ, Means NE. Glyphosate and glyphosate-resistant crop interactions with rhizosphere microorganisms. *Eur J Agron.* 2009;31:153–161

29 Liu Y, Li Y, Hua X, et al. Glyphosate application increases catabolic activity of gram negative bacteria but impaired

soil fungal community. *Environ Sci and Pollut Res Int.* 2018;9(15):14762–14772

30 Mills PJ, Kania-Korwel I, Fagen J, McEvoy LK, Laughlin GA, Barrett-Connor E. Excretion of the herbicide glyphosate in older adults between 1993 and 2016. *JAMA.* 2017;318(16):1610–1611

31 Parvez S, Gerona RR, Procter C, et al. Glyphosate exposure in pregnancy and shortened gestational length prospective Indiana birth cohort study. *Environ Health.* 2018;17:23

32 Sagener N. Overwhelming majority of Germans contaminated by glyphosate. *EurActive.* March 6, 2016. (Reporting on the study by Heinrich Böll Foundation)

33 Kusbad D, Nilsson EE, King SE, Sadler-Riggleman I, Beck D, Skinner MK. Assessment of glyphosate induced epigenetic transgenerational inheritance of pathologies and sperm epi-mutation: Generational Toxicology. *Sci Rep.* 2019;V9:6372

34 Champagne FA. Epigenetic mechanisms and the transgenerational effects of maternal care. *Front Neuroendocrinol.* 2008;29(3):386–397

35 Zhang L, Rana I, Shaffer RM, Taloli E, Sheppard L. Exposure to glyphosate-based herbicides and risk for non-Hodgkin lymphoma: a meta-analysis and supporting evidence. *Mutat Res.* 2019;781:186-206

36 Mill PJ, Caussy C, Loomba R. Glyphosate excretion is associated with steatohepatitis and advanced liver fibrosis in patients with fatty liver disease. *Clin Gastroenterol Hepatol.* 2020;18(3):741–743

37 Perumpail BJ, Ali Khan M, Yoo ER, Cholankeril G, Kim D, Ahmed A. Clinical epidemiology and disease burden of non-alcoholic fatty liver disease. *World J Gastroenterol.* 2017;23(47):8263–8276

38 Grander C, Grabherr F, Moschen AR, et al. Non-alcoholic fatty liver disease: cause or effect of metabolic syndrome. *Visc Med.* 2016;32:329–334

39 Persch TSP, Weimer RN, Freitas BS, Oliveira GT. Metabolic parameters and oxidative balance in juvenile rhamdia quelen

exposed to rice paddy herbicides: Roundup®, Primoleo®, and Facet®. *Chemosphere.* 2017;174:98–109

40 Mesnage R, Renney G, Seralini G, et al. Multiomics reveal non-alcoholic fatty liver disease in rats following chronic exposure to an ultra-low dose of Roundup herbicide. *Sci Rep.* 2017;7:39328

41 Lozano VL, Defarge N, Rocque LM, et al. Sex-dependent impact of Roundup on the rat gut microbiome. *Toxicol Rep.* 2017;5:96–107

42 Coumoul X, Servien R, Juricek L, et al. The GMO90+ project: absence of evidence for biologically meaningful effects of genetically modified maize-based diets on Wistar rats after 6-months feeding comparative trial. *Toxicol Sci.* 2019;168(2): 315–338

43 Mesnage R, Arno M, Seralini GE, Antoniou M. Transcriptome and metabolome analysis of liver and kidneys of rats chronically fed NK603 Roundup-tolerant genetically modified maize. *Environ Sci Eur.* 2017;29(1):6

44 Williams GM, Berry C, Burns M, de Carmargo JL, Greim H. Glyphosate rodent carcinogenicity bioassay expert panel review. *Crit Rev Toxicol.* 2016;46(supl):44–55

45 Pollan M. Big Food vs Big Insurance. *New York Times.* September 9, 2009

46 Lozano VL, Defarge N, Rocque LM, et al. Sex-dependent impact of Roundup on the rat gut microbiome. *Toxicol Rep.* 2017;5: 96–110

47 Mao Q, Manservisi F, Panzacchi S, et al. The Ramazzini Institute 13-week pilot study on glyphosate and Roundup administered at human-equivalent dose to Sprague Dawley rats: effects on the microbiome. *Environ Health.* 2018;17(1):50

48 Kubsad D, Nilsson EE, King SE, Saddler-Riggleman I, Beck D, Skinner MK. Assessment of glyphosate induced epigenetic transgenerational inheritance of pathologies and sperm epimutations: generational toxicology. *Sci Rep.* 2019;9(1):6372

49 De Long NE, Holloway AC. Early-life chemical exposures and risk of metabolic syndrome. *Diabetes, Metab Syndr Obes.* 2017;10:101–109

50 Cassels S. Overweight in the Pacific: links between foreign dependence, global food trade, and obesity in the Federated States of Micronesia. *Global Health.* 2006;2:10.

51 Hercberg S, Castetbon K, Czernichow S, et al. The Nutrinet-Santé Study: a web-based prospective study on the relationship between nutrition and health and determinants of dietary patterns and nutritional status. *BMC Public Health.* 2010;10(1): 242

52 Srour B, Fezeu LK, Kesse-Guyot E, et al. Ultra-processed food intake and risk of cardiovascular disease: prospective cohort study (NutriNet-Santé). *BMJ.* 2019;365:l1451

53 Fiolet T, Srour, B, Kesse-Guyot E, et al. Consumption of ultra-processed foods and cancer risk: results from NutriNet-Santé prospective cohort. *BMJ.* 2018;360:k322

54 Rico-Campà A, Martínez-González MA, Alverez-Alverez I, et al. Association between consumption of ultra-processed foods and all cause mortality: SUN prospective cohort study. *BMJ.* 2019;365:l1949

55 Mendonça RD, Pimenta AM, Gea A, et al. Ultra-processed food consumption and risk of overweight and obesity: the University of Navarra follow-up (SUN) cohort study. *Amer J Clin Nutr.* 2016;104(5):1433–1440

56 Mendonça RD, Lopes ACS, Pimenta AM, et al. Ultra-processed food consumption and the incidence of hypertension in a Mediterranean cohort: The Seguimiento Universidad de Navarra Project. *Am J Hypertens.* 2017;30(4):358–366

57 Kim H, Hu EA, Rebholz CM. Ultra-processed food intake and mortality in the USA: results from the third national health and nutrition examination survey (NHANES III, 1988-1994). *Public Health Nutr.* 2019;22(10):1777–1178

58 Kittle RP, McDermid KJ, Muehlstein L, Balazs GH. Effects of glyphosate herbicide on the gastrointestinal microflora of Hawaiian green turtles (Chelonia mydas) Linnaeus. *Mar Pollut Bull.* 2018;127:170–174

59 Amid C, Olstedt M, Gunnarsson JS, et al. Additive effects of the herbicide glyphosate and elevated temperature on the branched coral Acropora formosa in Nha Trang, Vietnam. *Environ Sci Pollut Res Int.* 2018;25(14):13360–13372

60 Mercurio P, Flores F, Mueller JF, Carter S, Negri A, Glyphosate persistence in seawater. *Mar Pollut Bull.* 2014;85(2):385–390

61 Kittle RP, McDermid KJ. Glyphosate herbicide toxicity to native Hawaiian macroalgal and seagrass species. *J Appl Phycol.* 2016;28(4):2597-2604

62 Lopes FM, Sandrini JZ, Souza MM. Toxicity induced by glyphosate and glyphosate-based herbicides in the zebrafish hepatocyte cell line (ZF-L). *Ecotoxicol Environ Saf.* 2018 Oct 30;162:201-207

63 Ma J, Zhu J, Wang W, Ruan P, Rajeshkumar S, Li X. Biochemical and molecular impacts of glyphosate-based herbicide on the gills of common carp. *Environ Pollut.* 2019 Sep;252(Pt B):1288-1300

64 Qin Y, Li X, Xiang Y, Wu D, Bai L, Li Z, Liang Y. Toxic effects of glyphosate on diploid and triploid fin cell lines from Misgurnus anguillicaudatus. *Chemosphere.* 2017 Aug;180:356-364

65 Weeks Santos S, Gonzalez P, Cormier B, et al. A glyphosate-based herbicide induces sub-lethal effects in early life stages and liver cell line of rainbow trout, Oncorhynchus mykiss. *Aquat Toxicol.* 2019 Nov;216:105291

66 Bridi D, Altenhofen S, Gonzalez JB, Reolon GK, Bonan CD. Glyphosate and Roundup® alter morphology and behavior in zebrafish. *Toxicology.* 2017 Dec 1;392:32-39

67 de Moura FR, da Silva Lima RR, da Cunha APS, et al. Effects of glyphosate-based herbicide on pintado da Amazônia: Hematology, histological aspects, metabolic parameters

and genotoxic potential. *Environ Toxicol Pharmacol.* 2017 Dec;56:241-248

68 Lopes FM, Caldas SS, Primel EG, da Rosa CE. Glyphosate adversely affects Danio rerio males: acetylcholinesterase modulation and oxidative stress. *Zebrafish.* 2017 Apr;14(2):97-105

69 Bókony V, Mikó Z, Móricz ÁM, Krüzselyi D, Hettyey A. Chronic exposure to a glyphosate-based herbicide makes toad larvae more toxic. *Proc Biol Sci.* 2017 Jul 12;284(1858):20170493

70 Berg CJ, King PH, Delenstarr G, Kumar R, Rubio F, Glaze T. Glyphosate residue concentrations in honey attributed through geospatial analysis to proximity of large-scale agriculture and transfer off-site by bees. *PLoS One.* 2018;13(7):e1098876

71 Seide VE, Bernardes RC, Pereira EJG, Lima MAP. Glyphosate is lethal and cry toxins alter the development of the stingless bee Melipona quadrifasciata. *Environ Pollut.* 2018;243(Pt B):1854–1860

72 Vázquez DE, Ilina N, Pagano EA, Zavala JA, Farina WM. Glyphosate affects the larval development of honey bees depending on the susceptibility of colonies. *PLoS One.* 2018;13(10):e0205074

73 Motta EVS, Raymanna K, Moran NA. Glyphosate perturbs the gut microbiota of honey bees. *Proc Natl Acad Sci U S A.* 2018;115(41):10305–10310

74 Faita MR, Oliveira EM, Viera V, Orth AI, Nodari RO. Changes in hypopharyngeal glands of nurse bees (Apis mellifera) induced by pollen-containing sublethal doses of the herbicide Roundup®. *Chemosphere.* 2018;211:566–572

75 Mengoni Goñalons C, Farina WM. Impaired associative learning after chronic exposure to pesticides in young adult honeybees. *J Experimental Biology.* 2018;221(7)

76 Balbuena MS, Tison L, Hahn ML, Greggers U, Menzelet R, Farina WM. Effects of sublethal doses of glyphosate on honeybee navigation. *J Exp Biol.* 2015;218(Pt 17): 2799–2805

77 Jumarie C, Aras P, Boily M. Mixtures of herbicides and metals affect the redox system of honey bees. *Chemosphere.* 2017;168:163–170

78 Karise R, Raimets R, Bartkevics V, et al. Are pesticide residues in honey related to oilseed rape treatments? *Chemosphere.* 2017;188:389–396

79 Berg CR, King PH, Delenstarr G, Kumar R, Rubio F, Glaze T. Glyphosate residue concentrations in honey attributed through geospatial analysis to proximity of large-scale agriculture and transfer off-site by bees. *PLoS One.* 2018;13(7):e0198876

80 Liao LH, Wu WY, Barenbaum MR. Behavioral responses of honey bees (Apis mellifera) to natural and synthetic xenobiotics in food. *Sci Rep.* 2017;7(1):15924

81 Boily M, Sarrasin B, Deblois C, Aras P, Chagnon M. Acetylcholinesterase in honey bees (Apis mellifera) exposed to neonicotinoids, atrazine and glyphosate: laboratory and field experiments. *Environ Sci Pollut Res Int.* 2013;20(8):5603–5614

82 Zhu YC, Yao J, Adamczyk J, Luttrell R. Feeding toxicity and impact of imidacloprid formulation and mixtures with six representative pesticides at residue concentrations on honey bee physiology (Apis mellifera). *PLoS One.* 2017;12(6):e0178421

83 Huang ZY, Hanley AV, Pett WL, Langenberger M, Duan JJ. Field and semifield evaluation of impacts of transgenic canola pollen on survival and development of worker honey bees. *J Econ Entomol.* 2004;97(5):1517–1523

84 Yerton S. Massive damage awards in previous cases are triggering a new onslaught against the chemical company. *Civil Beat.* August 29, 2019

85 Kogevinas Manolis. Probable carcinogenicity of glyphosate. *BMJ,* 2019; 365 :l1613

86 Myers JP, Antoniou MN, Blumberg B, et al. Concerns over use of glyphosate-based herbicides and risks associated with exposures: a consensus statement. *Environ Health.* 2016;15:19

87 Benbrook CM. How did the US EPA and IARC reach diametrically opposed conclusions on the genotoxicity of glyphosate-based herbicides? *Environ Sci Eur.* 2019;31:2

88 Depression and other common mental disorders: global health estimates. *Geneva: World Health Organization*; 2017

89 Weinberger AH, Gbedemah M, Martinez AM, et al. Trends in depression prevalence in the USA from 2005 to 2015: widening disparities in vulnerable groups. *Psychol Med.* 2018;48(8):1308–1315

90 Hedegaard H, Curtin SC, Warner M. Suicide rates in the United States continue to increase. *NCHS Data Brief.* June 2018;No. 309

91 Weingarten D, Why are American farmers killing themselves? *The Guardian.* Dec 11, 2018

92 Jones-Bitton A, Best C, MacTavish J, Fleming S, Hoy S. Stress, anxiety, depression, and resilience in Canadian farmers. *Soc Psychiatry Psychiatr Epidemiol.* 2019;55:229-236

93 Serrano-Medina A, Ugalde-Lizárraga A, Bojorquez-Cuevas MS, et al. Neuropsychiatric disorders in farmers associated with organophosphorus pesticide exposure in a rural village of Northwest México. *Int J Environ Res Public Health.* 2019;16(5):689

94 Suarez-Lopez JR, Hood N, Suarez-Torres J, Gahagan S, Gunnar MR, Lopez-Paredas D. Associations of acetylcholinesterase activity with depression and anxiety symptoms among adolescents growing up near pesticide spray sites. *Inter J Hyg Environ Health.* 2019;222(7):981–990

95 Mwabulambo SG, Mrema EJ, Ngowi AV, Mamuya SHD. Health symptoms associated with pesticides exposure among flower and onion pesticide applicators in Arusha region. *Ann Glob Health.* 2018;84(3):369–379

96 Koh SB, Kim TH, Min S, et al. Exposure to pesticide as a risk factor for depression: a population-based longitudinal study in Korea. *Neurotoxicology.* 2017;62:181–185

97 Aitbali Y, Ba-Mhamed S, Bennis M. Behavioral and immuno-histochemical study of the effects of subchronic and chronic exposure to glyphosate in mice. *Front Behav Neurosci.* 2017;11:146

98 Aitbali Y, Ba-M'hamed S, Elihidar N, Nafis A, Soraa N, Bennis M. Glyphosate-based- herbicide exposure affects gut microbiota, anxiety and depression-like behaviors in mice. *Neurotoxicol Teratol.* 2018;67:44–49

99 Cattani D, Cesconetto PA, Tavares MK, et al. Developmental exposure to glyphosate-based herbicide and depressive-like behavior in adult offspring: implication of glutamate excitotoxicity and oxidative stress. *Toxicology.* 2017;387:67–80

100 Martinez DA, Loening UE, Graham MC. Impacts of glyphosate-based herbicides on disease resistance and health of crops: A Review. *Environ Sci Eur.* 2018;30(1):2

101 Mertens M, Höss S, Neumann G, Afzal J, Reichenbecher W. Glyphosate, a chelating agent-relevant for ecological risk assessment? *Environ Sci Pollut Res Inter.* 2018;25(6):5298–5317

102 Van Bruggen AHC, He MM, Shin K, et al. Environmental and health effects of the herbicide glyphosate *Sci Total Environ.* 2018;616–617:255–268

103 Mann C. *The wizard and the prophet: two remarkable scientists and their dueling visions to shape tomorrow's world.* Unabridged. New York: Alfred A. Knopf; 2018

104 Slavikova SP. Advantages and disadvantages of monoculture farming. *Greentumble.* June 2019

105 Deener K. The Dose Makes the Poison-or does it? *The EPA Blog.* July 2014

106 Pollen M. *Food Rules: an eater's manual.* New York: Penguin Press; 2011

107 Pinto-Bazurco. Precautionary Principle. *2020 International Institute for Sustainable Development.* October 2020

108 Benbrook, C.M. Trends in glyphosate herbicide use in the United States and globally. *Environ Sci Eur.* 28, 3 (2016)

109 Davies S. Jury awards couple $2 billion in Roundup exposure case. *Agri-Pulse Com.* May 13, 2019

APPENDIX A

The following graphs are all from the following source: Swanson N, Leu A, Abrahamson J, et al. Genetically engineered crops, glyphosate and the deterioration of health in the United States of America. *J Org Syst.* 2014;9(2)

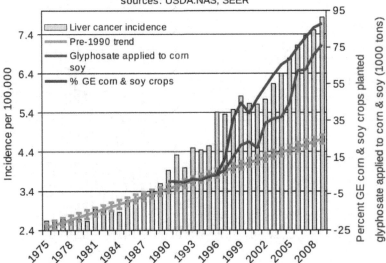

Liver and Intrahepatic Bile Duct Cancer Incidence (age adjusted)

plotted against glyphosate applied to corn & soy (R = 0.9596, p <= 4.624e-08) along with %GE corn & soy planted in U.S. (R = 0.9107, p <= 5.402e-05) sources: USDA:NAS; SEER

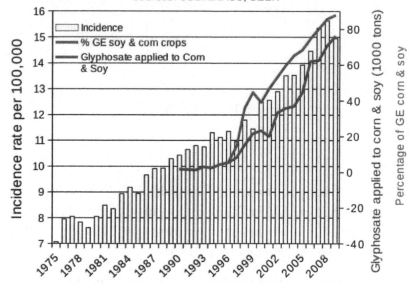

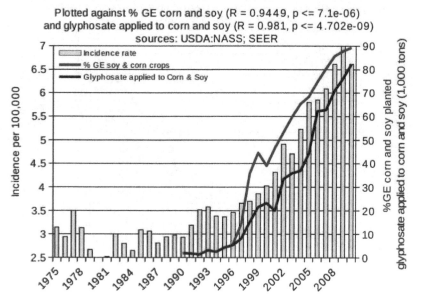

Thyroid Cancer Incidence Rate (age adjusted)

plotted against glyphosate applied to U.S. corn & soy (R = 0.988, p <= 7.612e-09)
along with %GE corn & soy crops R = 0.9377, p <= 2.152e-05
sources: USDA:NASS; SEER

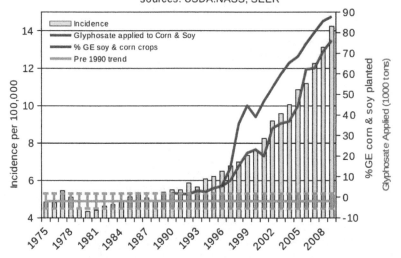

Age Adjusted Deaths due to Hypertension (ICD I10 & 401)

plotted against %GE corn and soy (R = 0.9607, p <= 3.675e-06)
& glyphosate applied to corn and soy (R = 0.923, p <= 1.603e-07)
Sources: USDA:NASS; CDC

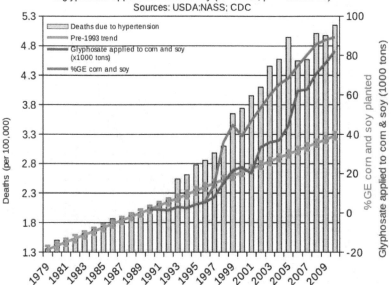

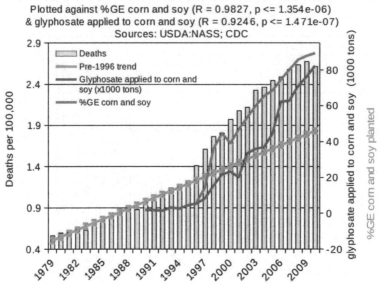

Age Adjusted Deaths due to Stroke
(ICD I62.9 & 432.9 hemorrhage, non embolic)

Plotted against %GE corn and soy (R = 0.9827, p <= 1.354e-06)
& glyphosate applied to corn and soy (R = 0.9246, p <= 1.471e-07)
Sources: USDA:NASS; CDC

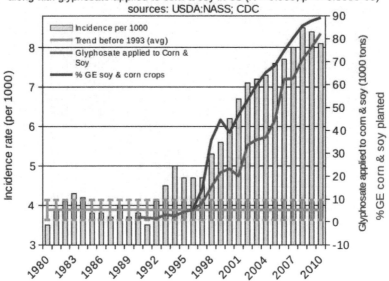

Annual Incidence of Diabetes (age adjusted)

plotted against %GE corn & soy crops planted (R = 0.9547, p <= 1.978e-06)
along with glyphosate applied to corn & soy in US (R = 0.935, p <= 8.303e-08)
sources: USDA:NASS; CDC

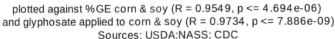

Age Adjusted Deaths due to Disorders of Lipoprotein Metabolism
(ICD E78.5 hyperlipoproteinemia & E78.0 hypercholesterolemia)

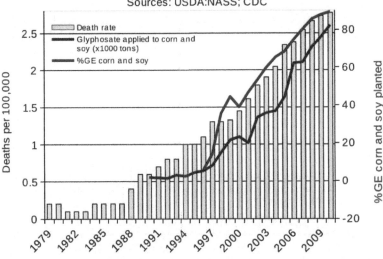

plotted against %GE corn & soy (R = 0.9549, p <= 4.694e-06)
and glyphosate applied to corn & soy (R = 0.9734, p <= 7.886e-09)
Sources: USDA:NASS; CDC

Age Adjusted End Stage Renal Disease Deaths
(ICD N18.0 & 585.6)
plotted against %GE corn & soy planted (R = 0.9578, p <= 4.165e-06)
and glyphosate applied to corn & soy (R = 0.9746, p <= 7.244e-09)
Sources: USDA:NASS; CDC

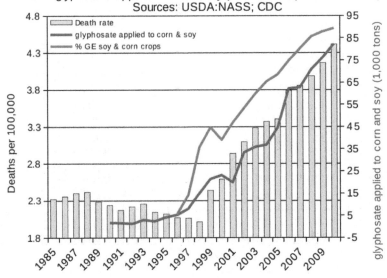

Hospital discharge diagnoses (any) of Inflammatory Bowel disease (Crohn's and Ulcerative Colitis ICD 555 & 556)

plotted against glyphosate applied to corn & soy (R = 0.9378, p <= 7.068e-08)
Sources: USDA & CDC

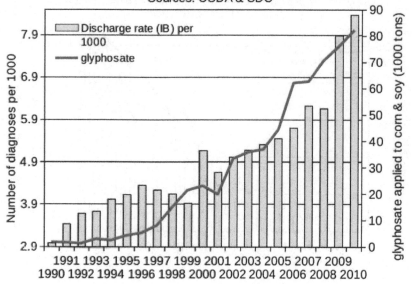

Age Adjusted Deaths due to Intestinal Infection (ICD A04, A09; 008, 009)

plotted against glyphosate applied to corn & soy (R = 0.9738, p <= 7.632e-09)
Sources USDA:NASS; CDC

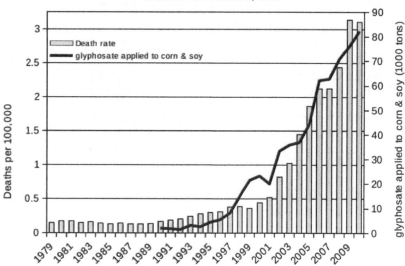

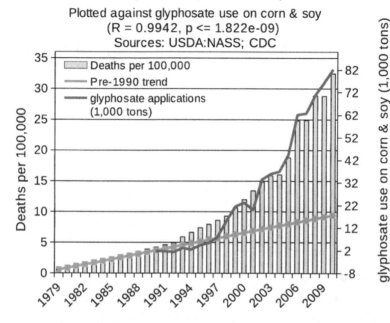

Age Adjusted Deaths from Senile Dementia
(ICD F01, F03 & 290)

Plotted against glyphosate use on corn & soy
(R = 0.9942, p <= 1.822e-09)
Sources: USDA:NASS; CDC

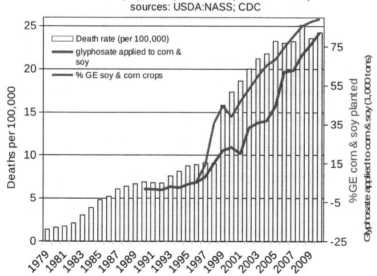

Age Adjusted Deaths from Alzheimer's (ICD G30.9 & 331.0)
Plotted against glyphosate use (R = 0.917, p <= 2.205e-07) &
%GE crops planted (R = 0.9373, p <= 9.604e-06)
sources: USDA:NASS; CDC

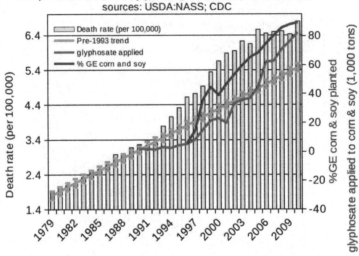

Age Adjusted Deaths from Parkinson's disease
(ICD G20 & 332.0)
plotted against glyphosate use on corn & soy (R = 0.8754, p <= 1.631e-06)
and percent GE corn & soy planted (R = 0.9516, p <= 5.398e-06)
sources: USDA:NASS; CDC

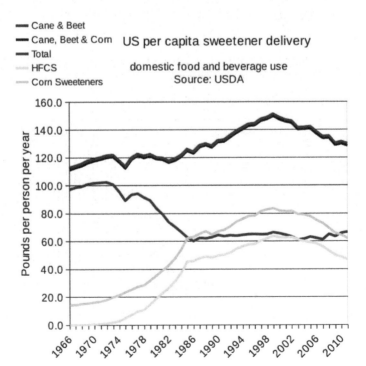

US per capita sweetener delivery
domestic food and beverage use
Source: USDA

Made in the USA
Coppell, TX
03 July 2022